Exam Skills Practice

Edexcel GCSE Business

Support

Student Workbook

Keith Hirst and Jonathan Shields

ALWAYS LEARNING

PEARSON

Published by Pearson Education Limited, a company incorporated in England and Wales, having its registered office at Edinburgh Gate, Harlow, Essex, CM20 2JE.
Registered company number: 872828
www.Pearsonschoolsandfecolleges.co.uk

Edexcel is a registered trademark of Edexcel Limited
Text © Pearson Education Limited 2011

First published 2011
15 14 13 12 11
10 9 8 7 6 5 4 3 2 1
British Library Cataloguing in Publication Data

A catalogue record for this book is available from the British Library
ISBN 978 1 446900 152 9

Typeset by Juice Creative
Cover design by Pearson Education Limited

Printed and bound at Ashford Colour Press, Gosport, Hants

Disclaimer
The material has been published on behalf of Edexcel and offers high-quality support for the delivery of Edexcel qualifications. This does not mean that this material is essential to achieve any Edexcel qualification, nor does it mean that this is the only suitable material available to support any Edexcel qualification. Edexcel material will not be used verbatim in setting any Edexcel examination or assessment. Any resource lists produced by Edexcel shall include this and other appropriate resources. Copies of official specifications for all Edexcel qualifications may be found on the Edexcel website: www.edexcel.com

Contents

About this book

This workbook has been written to help you practise your exam skills as you prepare for your GCSE Business Studies exam for either Unit 3 (Building a business) or Unit 5 (Introduction to economic understanding). You'll find practice activities for each question type you will face, helping you to understand what the examiner will be looking for in good answers. You'll find answers to the activities at the back of the book, so that you can check whether you're on track after you've completed the activities.

What to expect in the exam paper

The assessment for Units 3 and 5 is through an examination worth 90 marks. You have one and a half hours for this examination. The examination is divided into three sections which include a variety of question types, including multiple choice, short answer questions and extended response questions.

In this workbook, the Unit 3 and Unit 5 questions and activities have been colour-coded to help you quickly find the ones relevant to you. The Unit 3 pages are blue and Unit 5 pages are orange.

There are three sections on Unit 3 and 5 exam papers, and you must answer all questions in all three sections. Below is a summary of the different types of questions you can expect, and the pages in this book where information and activities can be found.

Summary of question types

Question type	Number of marks	Pages	I am confident with this ✓ / ✗
Objective test (multiple choice)	1 mark	6-8	
'Give', 'State' and 'Identify'	1–3 marks	9-11	
'What is meant by the term…?'	2 marks	12-14	
Questions using diagrams	1-4 marks	15-19	
'Calculate'	1-3 marks	20-24	
'Outline'	2-3 marks	25-31	
'Describe'	3-4 marks	32-38	
'Explain'	3 marks	39-45	
Choice	6 or 8 marks	46-54	
'Discuss'	6 or 8 marks	55-63	
'Assess'	8 or 10 marks	64-75	
'Using your knowledge of business/ economics, assess…'	10 marks	76-87	

How to use this book

This workbook has been planned to help you maximise your performance in your examination. Activities have been designed to enable you to build the skills that will help you to achieve: understanding the exam question, using the mark scheme, building an answer, writing under timed conditions, and improving existing answers.

For many of the activities you will write into the book itself. Space is provided to allow you to do this.

 Where you see this symbol you need to use a separate sheet of paper for the activity.

Where you see boxes like these, take note! They are there to help you or remind you of important information.

Introduction to objective test questions

Objective test questions feature in **Section A**. Each paper will usually have four such questions.

Objective test questions will be multiple choice. For each question you are given four possible answers. One of these is correct. Beware though. The wrong options – the **distracters** – have been chosen to appear as though they could be correct. Even if you think you know the right answer, read the other options as well.

A student who wishes to achieve a good grade should aim to correctly answer **all four** objective test questions.

A typical question

Business finance can come from either internal or external sources.

Which of the following is an internal source of finance? (1 mark)

*Select **one** answer.*

    A *A loan from a bank.*

    B *An overdraft.*

    C *Selling assets.*

    D *Selling shares.*

Strategies for getting the right answer

The following process can be used to improve your chances of getting the right answer.

- **Highlight** the key terms in the question. The question above refers to **internal** sources of finance. This can be easily confused with **external** sources.

- **Read** all the options carefully.

- **Rule out** those you know are wrong. For example, you may know that Option A – a loan from a bank – is wrong as this is an **external** source of finance. You might also know that Option B – an overdraft – is similar to a loan and is therefore also an external source of finance. By ruling out these two options, you have improved your chance of selecting the right answer.

- **Select** what you think is the right answer. As a business owns assets, selling them will raise finance. This finance comes from within the business and therefore C is the correct answer.

- **Check** D as well to ensure you are right. Selling shares is an external source of finance, so C is the correct answer.

Remember
Don't dive in! Think about each option before you make your decision.

Hint
Objective test questions generally test your knowledge of key terms. Make sure you actively learn your key terms as you are going through the course.

Activity 1: Understanding the exam question

Objective test questions are not necessarily easy. They are usually designed to test knowledge and understanding. One important strategy you can use is to make sure you can spot **distracters**.

In this activity you need to identify with a tick which of the options are 'good' distracters – those which sound as though they might be accurate but are not – and those which are 'bad' distracters – those which are obviously wrong.

One of the options listed below is the correct answer. When you have found it, place a tick next to it in the answer column.

Hint

Distracters are those options which are incorrect. They are phrased in such a way to make you **think** rather than being very obviously wrong.

Branding is important to a business' success because it… (1 mark)

	Options	Good	Bad	Answer
A	…will increase the business' costs.			
B	…involves having a logo and a slogan.			
C	…is the main reason why a business' profits will go up.			
D	…leads to more repeat purchases.			
E	…will reduce the business' cash outflows.			
F	…leads to less staff leaving.			

Activity 2: Build an answer

For the question below, write a correct answer plus three credible distracters. Highlight which one is the correct answer by placing a tick next to it in the answer column.

*Which of the following best describes the term '**salary**'?* (1 mark)

	Distracter/Correct answer	Answer
A		
B		
C		
D		

Activity 1: Understanding the exam question

Objective test questions are not necessarily easy. They are usually designed to test knowledge and understanding. One important strategy you can use is to make sure you can spot **distracters**.

In this activity you need to identify with a tick which of the options are 'good' distracters – those which sound as though they might be accurate but are not – and those which are 'bad' distracters – those which are obviously wrong.

One of the options listed below is the correct answer. When you have found it, place a tick next to it in the answer column.

Hint

Distracters are those options which are incorrect. These are phrased in such a way to make you **think**, rather than being very obviously wrong.

International trade is where countries import and export products.

Which of the following best describes an '**export**'? *(1 mark)*

Option		Good	Bad	Answer
A	A cost that a business needs to pay each month.			
B	A product made in another country.			
C	A tax imposed on products bought from foreign countries.			
D	An organisation which aims to influence business decisions.			
E	A product made in the UK and bought by a consumer in another country.			
F	Products only available in the UK.			

Activity 2: Build an answer

For the question below, write a correct answer plus three credible distracters. Highlight which one is the correct answer by placing a tick next to it in the answer column.

Which of the following best describes '**economies of scale**'? *(1 mark)*

Distracter/Correct answer		Answer
A		
B		
C		
D		

Introduction to 'Give', 'State' and 'Identify' questions

Questions that start with the words 'give', 'state' and 'identify' will usually be found in **Section A** of the exam paper. Some will also appear in Sections B and C.

To answer this kind of question you need to write a simple list of points. Don't use more than a few words. Each different point you make is worth one mark.

A student who wishes to achieve a good grade should aim to correctly answer **all** 'Give', 'State' and 'Identify' questions.

> **Hint**
> Make sure you write a list of different points. If the points you make are too similar, you will not get all of the marks.

How will I be marked?

You will gain 1 mark for each different point that you make.

A typical question

*Identify **two** methods Amazon might use to differentiate its service from its rivals. (2 marks)*

A 2-mark answer

Larger range of products.
Fast delivery.

Why does this answer gain 2 marks?

Two points are made and both points are different.

> **Hint**
> In questions like this, make sure that your two points are different enough. If you wrote:
>
> *1. New products.*
>
> *2. Bigger range of products.*
>
> You might only get 1 mark, because the two points you have made are too similar.

Activity 1: Using the mark scheme

Look at the question below:

> *Identify **two** methods of 'product trial' that Subway could use.*　　　(2 marks)

Now look at the mark scheme for this question:

> Award 1 mark for each appropriate response.
>
> Do not award a mark for very similar answers, e.g. advertising on ITV and advertising on Sky.

1. Use the mark scheme to mark Student A's answer below. Place your mark in the box below the answer.

Student A:

1. Subway could do lots of advertising, this will encourage lots of people to try their sandwiches for the first time and come to its shops.

2. Subway could offer money-off vouchers. This will make its sandwiches better value for money, meaning that more people will try them compared to other sandwich shops like Pret A Manger.

Mark awarded = ☐ /2

2. In the table below, place a tick(s) next to the potential problem(s) with Student A's answer:

Problem	Tick
Needs more points	
Too long	
Not clear enough	
Answer not applied to Subway	

3. Now use the mark scheme to mark Student B's answer. Place your mark in the box below:

Student B:

1. Offer free samples.

2. Low trial prices.

Mark awarded = ☐ /2

It is easy to get 2 marks in this kind of question. All you have to do is write a few words that answer the question and thus meet the command word 'identify'. Make sure you write two ideas that are different.

Activity 1: Using the mark scheme

Look at the question below:

*Identify **two** reasons why a business might want to grow.* (2 marks)

Now look at the mark scheme for this question:

Award 1 mark for each relevant reason:

- To increase profits.
- To increase market share.
- To take advantage of economies of scale.
- To gain more market power.

Do not award a mark for very similar answers, e.g. 'higher profit' and 'to make more money'.

1. Use the mark scheme to mark Student A's answer below. Place your score in the box below the answer.

Student A:

1. Businesses grow for many reasons. One important reason is that it might involve the business making more money (profit).

2. Another reason why a business may want to grow is to increase market share. This will mean that the business is able to charge higher prices as it has more market power over its competitors.

Mark awarded = [/2]

2. Use a highlighter pen to highlight exactly which parts of the answer scored the marks. Try and highlight as few words as possible that will still allow this answer to score full marks.

3. Now use the mark scheme to mark Student B's answer. Place your score in the box below the answer.

Student B:

1. Economies of scale.

2. Increased revenue.

Mark awarded = [/2]

Students that are aiming for a good grade often feel that they have to write lots for these questions. This is not the case. You can score full marks by only writing a few words. This will give you more time for the longer questions to come.

Introduction to 'What is meant by the term' questions

Questions that start with the words 'What is meant by the term…' will be found in **Sections B and C** of the exam paper and sometimes in Section A.

To answer this type of question you need to accurately define the term. Since the question is worth 2 marks you need to write an accurate definition or use an example.

A student who wishes to achieve a good grade should aim to score full marks on all 'What is meant by the term…' questions.

Hint

Ask your teacher for a copy of the specification. Only terms that appear in the specification can be asked in the examination.

A typical question

What is meant by the term **'pressure group'**? (2 marks)

A 2-mark answer

Pressure groups are organisations of people which seek to influence the decision-making of a firm or government.

Why does this answer gain 2 marks?

There is a clear understanding of what a pressure group is. The answer contains two parts: the fact that pressure groups are 'organisations of people' and that they are 'seeking to influence the decision-making of a firm or government'.

Remember

Even if you have not learnt the exact definition, try and extend your understanding of the term by writing an extra sentence or by giving an example.

For example, Greenpeace is a pressure group. Its members care about the environment and try and get the government to pass laws to reduce pollution.

This answer would also gain 2 marks.

Activity 1: Build an answer

Look at the question below:

> *What is meant by the term '**ethics**'?* *(2 marks)*

Now look at the mark scheme for this question:

> Two marks are given for a definition which includes two parts. Award 1 mark for reference to the term 'morals' or implying a sense of 'right'.
>
> Improving the answer to show what this means can improve the answer to 2 marks. This could take the form of an extra sentence which makes the definition clearer or by giving an example.

If you have learnt all the definitions of key terms in the specification, these questions are easy, since you will score two marks by just writing down what you have remembered. However, what if you panic and cannot remember the exact definition? Can you still get 2 marks for this kind of question?

Look at the answer below:

Student A:

Ethics is when a company does the right thing.

Using the mark scheme, how many marks would you give this answer?
Place your mark in the box below.

Mark awarded = | /2 |

Now try to improve the answer by writing an extra sentence or by giving an example.
Write your answer in the space below:

....

....

....

....

....

....

Remember

Always try and define the term and then give an example or an extra sentence. This can help you to score all of the marks.

Activity 1: Build an answer

Look at the question below:

> *What is meant by the term **'exchange rate'**?* (2 marks)

Now look at the mark scheme for this question:

> The market price at which one currency is sold in order to buy/exchange another currency.
>
> Award 2 marks for a definition that includes reference to both price and exchange/expression related to another currency.
>
> For 1 mark a limited definition is given such as 'The price of a currency' or '£1 = $1.60'.
>
> An imperfect definition can be raised to 2 marks through an extra clarifying sentence or example.

If you have learnt all the definitions of the key terms in the specification, these questions are easy, since you will score 2 marks by just writing down what you have remembered. However, what if you panic and cannot remember the exact definition? Can you still get 2 marks for this kind of question?

Look at the answer below:

Student A:

The exchange rate is how much a currency is worth.

Using the mark scheme, how many marks would you give this answer? Place your mark in the box below.

Mark awarded = [/2   ]

Now try to improve the answer by writing an extra sentence or by giving an example. Write your answer in the space below.

....

....

....

....

....

Remember
Always try and define the term and then give an example or an extra sentence. This can help you to score all of the marks.

....

Introduction to questions using diagrams

Some questions will require you to use a diagram. These questions are based on information contained in the diagram. They can appear in **Sections A, B or C**. Some diagrams require specific answers from the data. Others provide information on which to base more extended answers.

Examples of the type of diagrams you may be required to use are:

- break-even chart – Unit 3
- stock control – Unit 3
- product life cycle – Unit 3
- economic growth – Unit 5

A student who wishes to achieve a good grade should aim to score full marks on all diagram questions.

A typical question

Jason and Balvir have decided to use break-even analysis as part of the planning for their business. They are planning to offer a set menu for a price of £30.

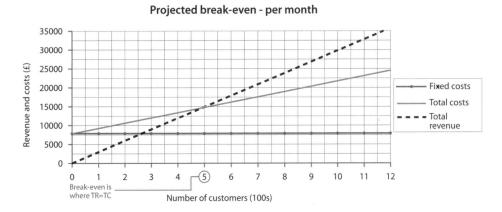

Projected break-even - per month

Using the graph above, how many customers do Jason and Balvir need to break even each month? (1 mark)

Strategies for getting the right answer

- **Thinking time:** Study the information carefully before you begin to answer.
- **Axes:** Make sure you understand what the axes show. Highlight the labels if necessary.
- **Write onto the diagram:** if you think this will help. In the diagram above, the student has circled in blue where they think the break-even point is. This might help you to work out the answer.
- **Units:** Make sure you provide the correct units with any answer you provide.

Break-even occurs where total revenue is equal to total costs. In this example, this point is at 500 customers.

Activity 1: Understanding the exam question

Bar gate stock charts give information on stock levels over time.

To use one, you need to find the appropriate distances on the diagram which relate to the amount of time or the amount of stock in question.

Look at the question below:

Tavistock Toy Chest is a small independent toy retailer.

The diagram below illustrates a bar gate stock chart for paddling pools at the Tavistock Toy Chest.

On the diagram there are four different coloured letters and distances.

- *Using the diagram, match the letter below with the correct explanation of the distance by drawing an arrow.*
- *Then match the explanation to the correct amount each line/distance represents.*
- *Distance A has already been done for you.* (*2 marks*)

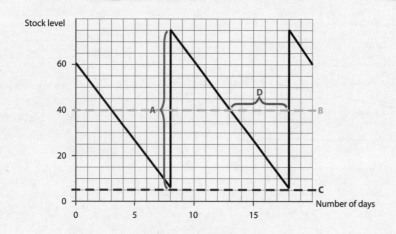

A	Re-order level of stock	5 pools
B	Size of order delivered on day 8	5 days
C	Time it takes stock to arrive after re-ordering	40 pools
D	Buffer stock	70 pools

Look at the question below:

Rattans Ltd is a business which makes and sells holiday souvenirs.

Last month Rattans Ltd sold 1000 souvenirs. Use the diagram below to calculate its margin of safety. Show your workings.

(2 marks)

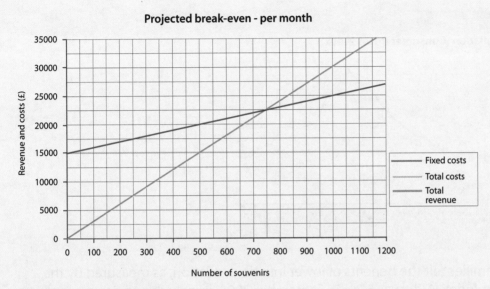

To answer the question:

- Start by finding out the amount that Rattans is currently producing. This figure is mentioned in the question. Place this figure in the green box below.

- Then you need to find the break-even level of output. This occurs where the total cost line crosses the total revenue line.

- Once you have found that point, you then need to read off the number of souvenirs, by drawing a vertical line down to the horizontal axis. Place this number in the purple box below.

- Now take the figure in the purple box away from the figure in the green box.

- Place your answer in the blue box. This figure is the margin of safety.

Margin of safety = _____ − _____ = _____ souvenirs.

Therefore, the formula for calculating the margin of safety is:

Margin of safety = ...

Activity 1: Understanding the exam question

If a question provides a diagram, you should spend some time making sense of the information it contains. You will then be able to use this information in the questions that follow.

*The diagram below shows UK inflation from 2007–2009. Study this data and identify **two** trends in the data. Provide reasons for the trends. An example is provided for you in the table below.*

(2 marks)

UK inflation (Consumer Prices Index)

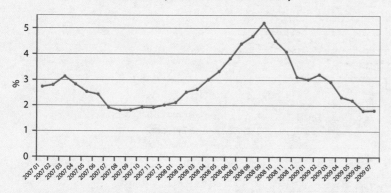

In 2009 many families felt the benefits of lower inflation. Inflation, as measured by the Consumer Prices Index (CPI), was 5.2% in September 2008, largely due to rising gas, electricity and food prices.

By September 2009 the CPI was 1.6%. One of the main reasons for the slowdown in inflation was a fall in the prices of basic items.

Hint
Look for where the biggest changes take place.

Answer the question in the table below.

Dates	Trend identified	Possible reasons
2007(3)–2007(8)	Inflation slows from 3% to just under 2%.	Less spending in the economy, possibly due to rising unemployment. People have less disposable income.

Activity 2: Understanding the exam question

Some questions will ask you to 'use an example' from the diagram.

Look at the question below:

The diagram below shows the exchange rate of the pound against the dollar from 2000–2007. Using an example from the graph, state what is meant by a 'strong pound'. (2 marks)

Exchange rate $ (US dollars) per £ (UK pound)

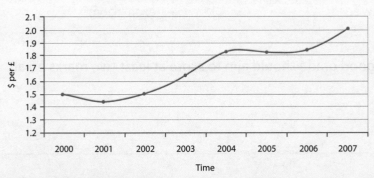

> **Hint**
>
> The question asks you to 'use an example'.

Look at the three student responses below and award each a mark. Give reasons to support your decision.

Response		Mark	Reason
A	A strong pound is where the pound grows in value.		
B	Where the pound will buy more dollars than it used to. For example, in 2001 £1 would buy $1.45 but in 2007 it would buy $2.00.		
C	Where the pound strengthens against foreign currencies. It means UK consumers get more dollars for every pound they spend. This is good for UK consumers as goods and services from the US become cheaper.		

Introduction to 'Calculate' questions

Questions that start with the word 'calculate' will usually be found in **Section B** of the exam paper.

'Calculate' questions involve using numbers and a formula. To get any marks at all, you have to learn your formulae.
You will get 1 mark for writing down the formula you use.

Once you have written down the formula, put the numbers given in the question into the formula. Doing this will get you a second mark because you have now shown your workings. Then use a calculator to work out the answer.
This will get you a third mark.

A student who wishes to achieve a good grade should aim to score at least two marks on all 'Calculate' questions.

Hint

Ask your teacher for a list of all the formulae you have studied. Make sure you learn them. This will make it much easier to do 'Calculate' questions in the exam room.

A typical question

Sony's fixed costs for the PlayStation® 3 are £2,400,000 and variable costs are £140 per console.

Calculate the break-even point when the PlayStation® 3 was priced at £300. Show your workings and the formula used. (3 marks)

A 3-mark answer

$$\text{Break-even} = \frac{\text{Total Fixed Costs}}{\text{Price} - \text{AVC}}$$

$$\text{Break-even} = \frac{£2,400,000}{(£300 - £140)}$$

$$\text{Break-even} = 15,000 \text{ consoles.}$$

Why does this response gain 3 marks?

The question asks you to state the formula and show your workings. This means that 1 mark is awarded for doing each of these things. The final mark is awarded for the answer.

Remember

Do not get scared by 'Calculate' questions. You will get 2 marks just for writing down the formula and putting the numbers from the question into the formula – even if you get the final answer wrong!

Activity 1: Using the mark scheme

Look at the question below:

Jason and Balvir have decided to use break-even analysis as part of the planning for their new restaurant. They are planning to offer a set menu for a price of £30.
They have estimated their costs as:

- *Fixed costs = £8,000*

- *Variable costs are £14 per set menu*

Calculate the break-even point. Give the formula and show your workings. **(3 marks)**

Now look at the mark scheme for this question:

1 mark for writing down the formula, 1 mark for showing your workings and 1 mark for the right answer.

$$\text{Break-even} = \frac{\text{Total fixed costs}}{(\text{Price} - \text{AVC})} \qquad \text{therefore} \qquad \text{Break-even} = \frac{£8000}{£30 - £14}$$

Break-even = 500 meals.

Use the mark scheme to mark the answer below. Place your mark in the box below the answer.

Student A:

Contribution per unit = £30 – £14 = £16

Total fixed costs = £8,000

Therefore break–even occurs at 500 meals.

Mark awarded = ☐ /3

In the table below, tick a box to highlight what was wrong with the answer.

Problem	Tick
No formula	
No workings	
Wrong answer	

Activity 2: Build an answer

Look at the question below:

Sony's fixed costs for the PlayStation® 3 are £2,400,000 and variable costs are £140 per console.

Calculate the level of profit or loss Sony would have made if it had sold 20,000 PlayStation® 3 consoles at £300. Show your workings and the formula used.   *(3 marks)*

Now look at the mark scheme for this question:

1 mark for writing down the formula, 1 mark for showing workings and 1 mark for writing down the correct answer.

Use the diagram below to help you plan your answer. The left-hand side of the diagram shows you the stages which you need to complete to get a mark. Answer the question by filling in the boxes on the right, so that you demonstrate three separate stages.

Write down the formula	Profit
Put numbers into the formula	Revenue = price x quantity sold = Total costs = fixed costs + variable costs =
Answer in units	Answer = £

If you follow this three-stage approach to answering 'Calculate' questions, you should always gain full marks (providing your maths is good and you have learnt the formulae!).

Activity 1: Build an answer

Note: 'Calculate' questions are **not** usually a feature of Unit 5. However, you do need to understand some numerical measurements. Specifically:

- price sensitivity
- productivity
- exchange rates
- total revenue
- total costs
- profit

Look at the question below:

> A football club charges an average of £20 per ticket. For a typical game the club has an attendance of 10,000.
>
> The club decides to increase its price to £25. Attendance at a typical game falls to 9,000.
>
> Use the idea of price sensitivity to suggest the most appropriate price for this business, if its objective was to increase revenue.   *(3 marks)*

To answer this question you first need to work out how much revenue the business has for each price:

Price = £20	Price = £25
Attendance = 10,000	Attendance = 9,000
Total revenue = 20 x 10,000 = £200,000	Total revenue = £25 x 9,000 = £225,000

So, revenue has increased as a result of this business increasing its price. Interesting. Note that the question asks you to, 'Use the idea of price sensitivity...'. In the space below, briefly outline which price the business should use. Fill in the gaps and delete the incorrect terms in bold.

> The business should charge £... This is because customers are price **sensitive/insensitive**.
>
> This can be shown because when the price was increased to £..., demand only fell by..
>
> As a result revenue **fell/increased**. The business should therefore charge the **lower/higher** price.

Activity 2: Build an answer

Look at the question below:

Charles Mitchell imports high quality pasta from Northern Italy for sale at his delicatessen in Suffolk. The exchange rate between the pound (£) and the euro (€) is important for Charles. He buys 100 kg of pasta every month. The price of pasta is €5 per kg.

In April, the exchange rate is £1.00 = €1.25. Calculate how much Charles has to pay to buy his pasta in this month.

(3 marks)

Now look at the mark scheme for this question:

1 mark for the identification of the formula, 1 mark for demonstrating workings and 1 mark for the correct answer.

Use the diagram below to help you plan your answer. The left-hand side of the diagram shows you the stages which you need to complete to get a mark. Answer the question by filling in the boxes on the right, so that you demonstrate three separate stages. The first box has been started for you.

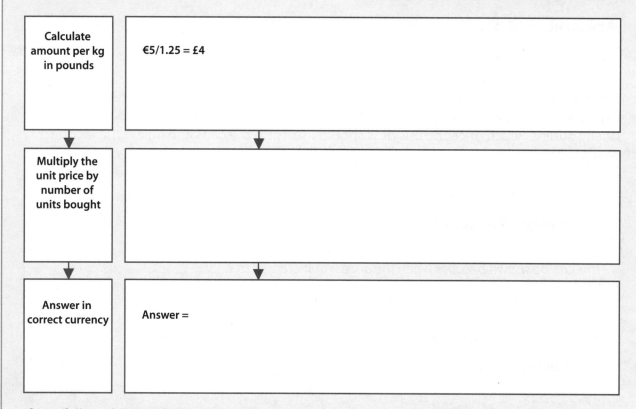

Calculate amount per kg in pounds	€5/1.25 = £4
Multiply the unit price by number of units bought	
Answer in correct currency	Answer =

If you follow this simple three-stage approach to answering 'Calculate' questions, you should always gain full marks (providing your maths is good and you have learnt the formulae!).

Introduction to 'Outline' questions

Questions that start with the word 'outline' will be found mostly in **Sections A and B** of the exam paper but possibly in Section C as well. These can be worth 2 or 3 marks.

To answer an 'Outline' question you need to take note of the number of marks available. Generally an 'Outline' question will be worth 2 marks, but could be worth 3. To answer these questions, you can make a number of points using sentences. These may be linked. In a 2-mark question you might make one point and develop it and, in a 3-mark question, you should make up to two points with one developed.

Where a question asks you to outline one factor or method, for example, the points you make should link to the factor or method you have identified. A list of points with no development will only score 1 mark.

A student wishing for a good grade should aim for full marks on this type of question.

> **Hint**
> It is a good idea to use an example to 'outline' a factor or method.

A typical question

*Outline **one** method a business might use to increase its profit. (2 marks)*

A 2-mark answer

Profits could be increased by cutting costs. If revenue stays the same, profits will rise.

Why does this answer gain 2 marks?

The point is made that 'cutting costs' will help to increase profits – this is the method. This scores 1 mark. A further mark is awarded for the development, which shows understanding of the relationship between costs, revenue and profit.

A 1-mark answer

Profits could be increased by selling more products. Also, the business could cut its costs.

> **Remember**
> If the question is worth 2 marks, you need to make one point and develop it.

Why does this answer only gain 1 mark?

The method given is 'selling more products' – this would gain 1 mark. The last sentence is a separate point. The question asks for **one** method only. This is a second method and therefore does not gain a further mark.

Activity 1: Using the mark scheme

Look at the question below:

> Outline **one** consumer protection law that Marks & Spencer must follow.   (2 marks)

Now look at the mark scheme below:

> 1 mark for the identification of one consumer protection law, and 1 mark for some kind of development or example using the Marks & Spencer context.

Mark the three student responses below.
There are 2 marks available for each question.

Hint

To answer an 'Outline' question worth 2 marks you should make one point and give some development using sentences. These may be linked. A list of points with no development will score only 1 mark.

Student A:

Sale of Goods Act.

Trades Description Act.

Mark awarded	Reasons

Student B:

Marks & Spencer must make sure that they follow the Trades Description Act. This means when they say on the label that a shirt is made out of cotton, it cannot be made out of nylon instead.

Mark awarded	Reasons

Student C:

Consumer protection laws stop people being ripped off by shops. They make sure that the prices of things aren't too high and that the quality of the things sold are really good.

Mark awarded	Reasons

Activity 2: Understanding the question

Read the following question. Then look at the different student responses in the table below.

> *Outline any problems a business might face by having too much stock.* (3 marks)

Decide whether the student provides statements which are developed by placing a tick in the second column. If there are no developing statements put a cross in the second column.

Use the third column to explain your reasons.

Hint

A developed statement builds on your first point. You need to offer some further explanation to demonstrate your understanding. Using an example is one way of offering development.

Response		Developed?	Reasons
A	By having too much stock you will need a bigger warehouse to store it in. Buying lots of stock also means you also have to spend lots of money buying it.		
B	By having too much stock you will need to have a bigger warehouse to store it in. This will mean that the business will face extra costs which will reduce its profits.		
C	By having too much stock you will increase your costs. You will also increase the amount of space you need to store the stock. All of the extra stock will also need to be insured in case the warehouse burns down.		

Activity 3: Improve an answer

Look at the question below:

*Outline **one** strategy Mars could use to extend the product life cycle of its Snickers bar.*

(3 marks)

Think about how the response below could be improved. The table suggests **possible** improvements. In the second column indicate with a tick or a cross whether each will improve this response. In the right-hand column offer one reason to support your decision.

Student A:

The product life cycle shows how the sales of a product will change over time. Mars could lower the price of the product so that more people will buy it, because it will be a better deal than buying a different product instead. When sales go up, the product life cycle has been extended.

	Suggested improvement	Does this help?	Reasons
1	Don't provide definitions of terms unless specifically asked.		
2	Provide more developed statements in the answer.		
3	Make sure the answer is worded around Snickers.		
4	Provide lots of detail, using as many concepts as possible.		
5	Provide as much information about the product life cycle as possible.		

Activity 4: Improve an answer

Read the answer below. Use the table to identify **two** strengths and **one** way in which the answer could be improved.

Student B:

Mars could launch a new version of Snickers with different types of nut in it. This new type of Snickers bar will interest people who would like to try the new bar. This would then result in more sales which would allow the product life cycle to become longer. However, Mars would need to do its market research first because some people are allergic to nuts.

Strengths	Area for improvement

Activity 1: Using the mark scheme

Look at the question below:

> *Outline how the government could reduce the level of unemployment in the economy.* (2 marks)

Now look at the mark scheme below.

> 1 mark for the identification of one measure the government could use, and 1 mark for some kind of development or example using the unemployment context.

Mark the three student responses to the question above. There are two marks available for each question.

Remember

To answer an 'Outline' question, you can make one point and give some development using sentences. These may be linked. A list of points with no development will only score 1 mark.

Student A:

Taxes

Lower interest rates

Investment

Mark awarded	Reasons

Student B:

The government could reduce unemployment by lowering taxes. This would give people more money to spend and so businesses would have to take on more workers.

Mark awarded	Reasons

Student C:

Unemployment is where some people don't have jobs. This can mean they end up in poverty and have a poor standard of living. The government needs to take action to keep unemployment to a minimum.

Mark awarded	Reasons

Activity 2: Understanding the question

For the following question, look at the different student responses in the table below.

*Outline **one** problem a business may face by growing too large.* *(2 marks)*

Decide whether the student provides statements which are developed by placing a tick in the second column. If there are no developing statements, put a cross in the second column. Use the third column to explain your reasons.

Hint

A developed statement builds on your first point. You need to offer some further explanation to demonstrate your understanding. Using an example is one way of offering development.

	Response	Developed?	Reasons
A	If a business gets too big its costs will rise. Also, growing in size will make the business difficult to manage.		
B	By growing in size the business will have more employees. This will mean that the business is more difficult to manage.		
C	By being too big a business will have high costs. However, it will also have economies of scale and so it will not all be bad news. This is an example of economies of scale.		

Activity 3: Improve an answer

Look at the question below:

*Outline **one** way in which a strengthening of the exchange rate of the pound could affect a UK exporter.* *(2 marks)*

Think about how the response below could be improved. The table suggests **possible** improvements to the response. In the second column indicate with a tick or a cross whether this will improve each response. In the right-hand column offer one reason to support your decision.

Student A:

A strengthening of the exchange rate means that the pound will buy more of a foreign currency. By strengthening in value exporters will be at a disadvantage. This is because their products will cost more for foreign customers. But it will mean that imports are cheaper.

	Suggested improvement	Does this help?	Reasons
1	Don't provide definitions of terms unless asked for.		
2	Link together different parts of the explanation.		
3	Use paragraphs to organise the answer.		
4	Provide lots of detail, using as many concepts as possible.		
5	Provide one point and develop it.		

Now write an answer which is more appropriate and would get you the 2 marks:

....

....

....

Activity 4: Improve an answer

Read the answer below. Use the table to identify **two** strengths and **two** weaknesses.

Student B:

The business will suffer as foreign consumers will face lower prices. Demand will therefore rise which may cause profit to rise. Rising profit may well lead to the business having more money to reinvest.

Strengths	Weaknesses

Introduction to 'Describe' questions

Questions that start with the word 'describe' will be found mostly in **Sections A and B** of the exam paper. To answer you need to make a number of unrelated points using sentences:

- In a 3-mark question you need to make three points, or one/two points with some development.

- In a 4-mark question, you need to make four points or two points with some development of each.

- 'Describe' questions allow you to use a definition as one.

Most, but not all, 'Describe' questions refer to a particular business. These questions must be answered in the context of that business to score well. This means that your answer must be capable of being linked to the particular business in the evidence not just **any** business.

A student who wishes to achieve a good grade should aim to score at least 2/3 or 3/4 marks on all 'Describe' questions.

> **Hint**
> To help put an answer into context, think about the kind of product the business makes and who its competitors are. For example, Sports Direct sell football kit and trainers and its competitors are JJB Sports and JD Sports. By mentioning this type of thing in your answer you have increased the chance of applying your knowledge to the question.

A typical question without context

Describe why branding might be important to a business. (3 marks)

A 2-mark answer

Branding gives a business a clearer identity and personality. A brand is important because it makes your product stand out.

Why does this response gain 2 marks?

There are two sentences. Each sentence says something different about why branding is important to a business. One of the sentences in the answer is a definition.

A typical question with context

Describe why developing a well known brand is important to the success of a business such as Amazon. (3 marks)

A 2-mark answer

Branding gives Amazon a clear identity and personality. Branding allows Amazon to stand out because there is lots of competition on the Internet.

Why does this response gain 2 marks?

There are two sentences. Each sentence says something different about why branding is important to Amazon. The answer is also applied to Amazon because the Internet is mentioned and Amazon only sell books, etc., on the Internet.

Activity 1: Using the mark scheme

Look at the question below:

Describe why it is important for Subway to differentiate its products.　　　(3 marks)

Now look at the mark scheme for this question:

For 3 marks, development will clearly show the importance of product differentiation to Subway. Within the answer there will be three points made or two points with one being developed, with the answer rooted in the Subway/sandwich/fast food context. 2 marks are awarded for the points/development and 1 mark is awarded for the use of context.

Possible answers include:

- Increases sales/market share.
- Stands out against rivals, e.g. McDonald's.
- Enables the firm to add value.
- Allows the firm to charge higher prices without the loss of demand.
- Makes it harder for a new firm to set up in competition.
- Helps build a strong brand presence.

Use the mark scheme to mark the answer below. Place your score in the box below the answer.

Student A:

Differentiation allows a firm's products to stand out in the market place which means that the product is seen as being different or better than the competition. It can also give a firm a unique selling point.

Mark awarded = ☐ /3

Use the table below to show how this answer could be improved. Place a tick next to each **main** improvement you think is necessary.

Problem	Tick
Needs more points	
Could be shorter	
Needs to be clearer	
Answer needs to be worded around Subway	

Activity 2: Improve an answer

In the previous activity we looked at the following question:

Describe why it is important for Subway to differentiate its products. (3 marks)

Student A:

Differentiation allows a firm's products to stand out in the market. This means that the product is seen as being different or better than the competition. It also gives a business a unique selling point.

Examiner's comments:

The answer scored 2 marks, since a point was made with some development and this was followed by another unrelated but relevant point. However the answer made no reference to Subway at all and, because Subway was mentioned in the question, marks will be awarded for applying your answer to the business stated.

In the student's answer, some words have been highlighted in yellow. It is possible to replace these highlighted words with new words that will improve the answer, allowing it to be applied to what Subway does.

Fill in the gaps in the answer below with new words that will apply the answer to the Subway context. The first two gaps have been completed for you in red. The other words to use are in the box below:

sandwich	**sandwiches**	**healthy**	**Subway's**
baguettes	**McDonald's**	**market**	

Differentiation allows Subway's baguettes to stand out in the ....

This means that its ....

are seen as being different or better than the competition

like ....

Providing ....

can also give Subway a unique selling point.

> **Hint**
> In questions that include the name of a business, you must apply your answer to the business in question. This is an easy way to get extra marks.

Activity 3: Write an answer

Look at the questions below:

> **Question 1:**
>
> *Describe a benefit to a business of improved worker motivation.* (3 marks)
>
> **Question 2:**
>
> *Describe why a strong brand might be important to Apple.* (3 marks)

There is an **important difference** between these two questions and how they will be marked. Look at the table below. Place a tick next to the main difference.

Main difference	Tick
Question 1 is harder	
Question 2 is harder	
Question 2 mentions Apple	

You need to remember the following things when writing an answer to a 'Describe' question:

- You need to write two to three separate points, in sentences that do not need to be linked, although one point may be developed.

- You can use a definition as one of the points.

- In questions that refer to the name of a business, you need to apply your answer to that business.

 On a separate piece of paper, write an answer to both of these questions. Give yourself no longer than three minutes to answer each question. Try to make sure you score at least 2 marks in each answer.

You or a friend can now mark the answers using the mark scheme on page 92 at the back of the book.

Activity 1: Using the mark scheme

Look at the question below:

Describe the possible disadvantages for a business when it grows in size. (3 marks)

Now look at the mark scheme for this question:

For 3 marks, development will clearly show understanding of the disadvantages of business growth. Within the answer there will be three points made or two points with one being developed.

Possible answers include:

- Potential problems if the business grows too quickly or becomes too 'big'.
- Possible diseconomies of scale as average costs of production rise.
- Increases in costs coincide with a less than proportionate increase in output.
- Businesses may be forced to increase prices.
- More difficult to manage.
- Communications more difficult.

Use the mark scheme to mark the answer below. Place your score in the box below the answer.

Student A:

One disadvantage of a business growing in size is its costs will rise. As the business grows it will be too big to manage and its costs will rise.

Mark awarded = [   ] /3

Remember

This question provides no context for you to tailor your answer to: it refers only to 'a business'.

Use the table below to show how this answer could be improved. Place a tick next to each **main** improvement you think is necessary.

Improvement	Tick
Needs more points	
Could be shorter	
Needs to be clearer	
Answer needs to be worded around business growth	

Activity 2: Improve an answer

Look at the question below:

> *Describe how a strengthening of the pound against other currencies might affect a UK export business.*
> *(4 marks)*

Student A:

The exchange rate is how much one currency is worth in terms of another. If the exchange rate strengthens £1 will buy more of a foreign currency. Exporters will suffer, however, as their product will now cost more for foreign customers. This will also help importers who will be able to buy foreign goods more cheaply.

Examiner's comments:

The answer scored 3 marks, since a definition was provided (1 mark) plus two valid points about how a UK exporter will be affected. However, the answer does not focus on an exporter. The last sentence states how an importer might be affected. This is not the question!

It is possible to rewrite the answer, allowing it to be worded around what **an exporter** does.

Fill in the gaps in the answer below with new words that will link the answer to the context of a UK export business. Use six of the words given below to help you build this answer.

Hint

Take care – some of these words are intended to trick you!

fixed	more expensive	benefit	bad
variable	good	cheaper	fall

A strong pound is .... for an exporter. This is because their

goods will be .... for foreign customers. If the exporter has to

import components or raw materials, however, it will .... from

the strong pound. This is because imports will now be ....

This will cause costs to ....

Remember

In questions that include the name of a business, or a specific business context, you must apply your answer to this context. This is one of the main reasons why good students do not gain full marks in 'Describe' questions.

Activity 3: Write an answer

Look at the questions below:

Question 1:

Describe a benefit to a business of low interest rates. (3 marks)

Question 2:

Describe how a business like McDonald's might measure its success. (3 marks)

There is an **important difference** between these two questions and how they will be marked. Look at the table below. Place a tick next to the main difference.

Main difference	Tick
Question 1 is harder	
Question 2 is harder	
Question 2 mentions McDonald's	

You need to remember the following things when writing an answer to a 'Describe' question:

○ You need to write two to three separate points in sentences that do not need to be linked, although one point may be developed.

○ You can use a definition as one of the points.

○ In questions that refer to the name of a business, you need to apply your answer to that business.

 On a separate piece of paper write an answer to both of these questions.
Give yourself no longer than three minutes to answer each question.

You or a friend can now mark the answers using the mark scheme on page 92 at the back of the book.

Introduction to 'Explain' questions

Questions starting with the word 'explain' will be found in **all sections** of the exam paper.

To answer an 'Explain' question you need to make a number of points using sentences. Each sentence needs to be linked together using words like 'because', 'this leads to' and 'as a result'. All 'Explain' questions are worth 3 marks. Giving a definition at the start of your answer **does not** allow you to score a mark.

Most 'Explain' questions mention the name of a business. To answer these questions you must try and write something about that business in your answer which helps to answer the question. This is called putting your answer into context.

A student wishing to achieve a good grade should aim to score at least two marks on an 'Explain' question.

A typical question without context

Explain why an increase in the rate of interest might lead to a reduction in inflation. (3 marks)

A 2-mark answer

Raising interest rates will make loans more expensive, **which means** fewer people borrow money.

Why does this response gain 2 marks?

There is one sentence which provides a linked point. The answer uses connective words which are highlighted in bold in the answer. The third mark would have been given if another sentence was given linking the number of people borrowing money with inflation.

A typical question with context

*Explain **one** benefit to Sony of improving its productivity. (3 marks)*

A 2-mark answer

Increasing productivity means Sony can make more TVs in an hour. **This means** that Sony is becoming more efficient in making TVs.

Why does this answer gain 2 marks?

There are two sentences. Each sentence is linked together using the connective words highlighted in bold. The answer is worded around the kinds of products Sony make.

Activity 1: Understanding the exam question

The command word 'explain' is different to the command word 'describe'.

In order to meet the command word 'explain', sentences need to be **linked together** to answer the question. **A definition will not be awarded any marks**. This is because an explain question requires you to also demonstrate higher order skills of application and analysis rather than simply giving knowledge.

Look at the question below:

> *Explain **one** benefit to a business such as McDonald's of using a Just In Time (JIT) method of stock control.* *(3 marks)*

In order to score three marks, you will need to do the following:

- Identify **one** benefit.

- Use two sentences to explain how it will benefit McDonald's.

- Make sure you apply your answer to McDonald's or a similar fast-food restaurant.

Choose one benefit from box 1 below.

Box 1: Benefits

1. Allows McDonald's to have better relationships with meat suppliers.

2. Reduces McDonald's costs.

3. McDonald's cash flow will be improved.

Now choose **two** linking sentences from box 2 below, that explains the benefit you chose in box 1.

Box 2: Linked explanation sentences

1. Therefore less money is tied up in stocks of burgers.

2. As a result, there will be more trust between them and McDonald's.

3. Therefore smaller, cheaper restaurants can be built.

4. This is because less space is needed to store frozen burgers.

5. This is because less stock of burgers, baps, etc., need to be purchased.

6. This is because meat suppliers will have to deliver on time.

 Now write down your three-sentence answer on a piece of paper to make sure that it makes sense. With a highlighter pen, go back and highlight the way in which you have ensured your answer is applied to McDonald's or a similar fast-food restaurant.

Activity 2: Using the mark scheme

Look at the question below:

> *Explain why strong cash flow is important to a supermarket such as Lidl.* (3 marks)

Now look at the mark scheme for this question:

For 3 marks, development will clearly show the importance of strong cash flow. Within the answer there will be at least two clearly identifiable strands of explanation with the answer applied to a Lidl/supermarket context. Two marks are awarded for the links and 1 mark is awarded for the use of context.

Possible answers include:

- Prevents failure (especially in recession).
- Prevents the need for loans/overdrafts.
- Can pay bills when they fall due.
- Improves financial management.
- Improves liquidity/working capital (although this is not on the specification, it could be an answer some candidates give and would be credited).

Use the mark scheme to mark the answer below. Place your score in the box below the answer.

Student A:

Cash flow is the record of cash inflows and cash outflows over time. Having strong cash flow will make it less likely that Lidl will run out of cash.

Mark awarded = [/3]

Hint

If you can replace the word 'Lidl' in the answer with any other business and the answer makes sense then it is likely it is not answered in context.

In the table below, tick the way(s) the answer could be improved:

Improvement	Tick
Needs more linking sentences	
Could be shorter	
Answer needs to be applied to Lidl	
Doesn't need a definition	

Activity 3: Improve an answer

Look at the question below:

> *Explain* **one** *benefit to Co-operative Food of being an ethical business.*   (3 marks)

Student A:

Being ethical means that Co-operative Food tries to do the right thing at all times. For instance Co-operative Food sells FairTrade food which plays fair by farmers living in poor countries. Being ethical is important because it means that the world is not polluted and people are not exploited. Being ethical will improve Co-operative Food's image.

Examiner's comments:

The answer is too long and the student could have scored more marks with a shorter answer which is more focused around the word 'explain'. The student offers a definition of 'ethical' and gives an example, but the question is not asking for him/her to define the term. However, the example does put the answer into the Co-operative Food context which allows the student to score a mark. The final sentence which states that 'being ethical will improve Co-operative Food's image' also scores a mark because this is one of the reasons why being ethical is important to Co-operative Food. The second to last sentence does not get any marks because this is not a benefit to Co-operative Food. This student has scored 2/3 marks because they did not put enough linked sentences into their answer.

This answer could be improved if the student had:

- started by highlighting **one** benefit to Co-operative Food of being ethical

- then written two linked sentences of explanation, one after the other

- made sure they applied their answer to Co-operative Food/supermarkets.

Remember

To make sure your answer is applied to Co-operative Food, think about what Co-operative Food sells and who its competition is. The student's answer above mentioned FairTrade food.

Using the final sentence of the student's answer as your starting point, improve this answer so that it gains full marks, by explaining why being ethical will benefit Co-operative Food.

Being ethical will improve Co-operative Food's image. This is because:

....

....

As a result, Co-operative Food can:

....

....

Activity 1: Understanding the exam question

The command word 'explain' is different to the command word 'describe'.

In order to meet the command word 'explain', sentences need to be **linked together** to answer the question. **A definition will not be awarded any marks**. This is because an explain question requires you to also demonstrate higher order skills of application and analysis rather than simply giving knowledge.

Look at the question below:

> *Explain **one** way in which a business might benefit from economies of scale. (3 marks)*

In order to score 3 marks, you will need to do the following:

- Identify **one** way.

- Use two sentences to explain how this will benefit a business.

Choose **one** benefit from box 1 below:

Box 1: Benefits

- The business will be able to lower average costs.

- The business will be able to buy in bulk.

- The business will be able to charge lower prices for its products.

Now choose **two** linking sentences from box 2 below, that explains the benefit you chose in box 1.

Box 2: Linked explanation sentences

1. Therefore it will be able to charge lower prices for its product.
2. This is because it is operating on a larger scale.
3. Therefore it can can buy each unit more cheaply.
4. As a result the business may become more competitive.
5. As a result this will reduce the average cost of making each unit of output.
6. This is because average costs of production will be lower.

 Now write down your three-sentence answer on a piece of paper to make sure that it makes sense. With a highlighter pen now go back and highlight any evidence that the answer you just constructed relates to economies of scale.

Activity 2: Using the mark scheme

Look at the question below:

> The Single European Market (SEM) in the European Union (EU) has led to the development of free trade between its members. It has led to an improvement in living standards amongst member countries. The EU places trade restrictions on non-member countries. Explain **one** reason why the EU might want to restrict trade. *(3 marks)*

Now look at the mark scheme for this question:

> For 3 marks, development will clearly show the importance of trade restrictions. Within the answer there will be at least two clearly identifiable strands of explanation with the answer rooted in an EU context. One mark is awarded for identifying the reason and two marks for the links made which are in context.
>
> Possible reasons include:
>
> - To encourage the free movement of goods and services only between members.
> - To stop the inflow of goods and services which might threaten infant industries.
> - Free trade threatens the standard of living of member populations.
> - To maintain employment.

Use the mark scheme to mark the answer below. Place your score in the box below the answer.

Student A:

The EU is a region which allows free trade between member states to take place. The EU restricts trade so employment in member countries is high and therefore standard of living is high.

Mark awarded = [/3   ]

In the table below, tick the way(s) the answer could be improved:

Improvement	Tick
Don't provide a definition	
Could be shorter	
Answer needs to be worded around the EU	
Needs more linking sentences	

Activity 3: Improve an answer

Look at the question below:

*Explain **one** effect of inflation on a business.*   *(3 marks)*

Student A:

Inflation is the general rise in prices in an economy. The UK has an inflation target of 2%. If it increases above this level then the Bank of England will increase interest rates. One effect of high interest rates is that loans become more expensive for businesses. One impact of high inflation on a business is that its running costs are likely to increase.

Examiner's comments:

The answer is too long and the student could have scored more marks with a shorter answer which is more focused on the question. The student offers an excellent definition of what inflation means, but the question is not asking for a definition of the term. The only part of the answer which scores any marks is the final sentence which states that 'its running costs are likely to increase'. The preceding sentences refer to the effect of higher interest rates. This does not get any marks because this is not specific to the effects of inflation. This is a potentially good student who has scored 1/3 marks because they did not understand what the word 'explain' required them to do.

This answer could be improved if the student had:

○ started by highlighting **one** effect of inflation on a business

○ written two linked sentences of explanation

○ made sure they applied their answer to the effect on a business.

Using the final sentence of the student's answer as your starting point, improve this answer so that it gains full marks, by explaining how inflation will affect a business. You might use some of these words in your answer:

| *reduced* | *customers* | *profit margin* | *prices* |

One impact of high inflation on a business is that its running costs are likely to increase.

This may mean that ....

....

....

Because of this ....

....

....

....

Remember
Stay focused! Think about the effects of inflation – rising prices – **on a business**.

Introduction to choice questions

Section A or Section B will often include at least one choice question which is worth 6 (or sometimes 8) marks. The first part of the question provides the business context. The second part asks you to decide which is the best method or factor from the context. There is **no** right or wrong answer in terms of the choice you make. It's up to you – so long as you can **justify** your decision.

How will I be marked?

This question is worth 6 marks. Any student who wishes to achieve a good grade should aim to get at least 4 marks on this type of question. To get 4 marks you need to:

- make a decision

- give at least one developed explanation containing linked statements which help to justify your decision

- use appropriate business concepts and terms.

> **Hint**
> It is a good idea to organise your response using paragraphs.

You can refer to both methods in your answer – but you do not need to do this to get full marks.

A typical question

Improving the quality of a product and improving productivity are two ways in which a business like McDonald's might become more competitive.

Which of these two methods do you think would be most effective in improving the competitiveness of a business such as McDonald's and why? (6 marks)

A 4-mark answer

McDonald's should choose to improve productivity in its restaurants. It could do this by training its workers to do jobs more quickly, which will mean customers will be served more quickly. This means customers will have a good impression of McDonald's and may go back there, therefore helping McDonald's to become more competitive.

Why does this response gain 4 marks?

This response gets 4 marks because the student explains one reason why increasing productivity will enable McDonald's to become more competitive. The explanation is made up of linked statements, and makes use of linking phrases. Some business terms are used. The student then provides a summary conclusion based on the analysis. By offering a linked explanation of one method and by providing some explanation through giving reasons which are relevant to McDonald's, the student gets to the top of Level 2.

> **Remember**
> There is no right or wrong answer. You can gain marks by arguing for either of the two methods. If you had approached this by explaining why improving quality would be a better strategy than higher productivity then this could also gain 6 marks.

Note: if you have an 8-mark choice question, exactly the same principles apply as detailed above, but you may need to provide a more developed conclusion in context. Any student who is aiming to achieve a good grade should be aiming to get at least 5 marks in an 8-mark question.

Activity 1: Understanding the exam question

Look at the question below:

Improving the quality of a product and improving productivity are two ways in which a business like McDonald's might become more competitive.

Which of these two methods do you think would be most effective in improving the competitiveness of a business such as McDonald's and why? (6 marks)

The best way to build your answer to this type of question is to use the same techniques as for 'Explain' questions (see page 39). Building an answer using linking words or phrases, such as 'because' and 'this will mean', will help you to structure your ideas and provide analysis through giving reasons/causes/consequences.

In the space below there is an incomplete answer. Use the linking words and phrases to complete the answer.

therefore	*as a result*	*because*

Increasing productivity will be the best way of increasing McDonald's competitiveness

.... it is a fast-food restaurant. .... it needs to deliver the burgers fast.

.... having burgers ready means that people will choose McDonald's instead

of Burger King.

Activity 2: Build an answer

Look at the three student responses in the table below. The first part of each answer is highlighted in yellow and the second part is highlighted in blue.

Indicate with a tick in the final column whether the second part is linked to the first part of the answer. If it is not, use a cross .

	Response	Linked?
A	Productivity is the output of burgers per worker per hour. Productivity increases the speed with which tasks are done.	
B	Productivity is the amount of burgers McDonald's can make in a period of time. If McDonald's increase productivity, it can supply more burgers, allowing more customers to be served.	
C	Productivity increases the speed with which things can be done. This means that the waiting time will be shorter. As a result, customers will prefer McDonald's to Burger King.	

Activity 3: Using the mark scheme

Look at the question again:

> Improving the quality of a product and improving productivity are two ways in which a business like McDonald's might become more competitive.
>
> Which of these two methods do you think would be most effective in improving the competitiveness of a business such as McDonald's and why? *(6 marks)*

Now look at the mark scheme for this question:

Mark	Descriptor
1	Simple judgement given about which is the best method. No development is given, or it is very simplistic.
2	Judgement is given with some simple development.
3	Judgement is given on one or both methods with some development/support, which includes at least one reason/cause/consequence, etc.
4	A judgement is given on one or both methods with some development/support, which includes at least one reason/cause/consequence, etc. Answer will refer to the McDonald's/fast-food context.

Use the mark scheme to mark the answer below. Place your score in the box below, explaining your reasons.

Student A:

Improving the quality of the burgers at McDonald's will be most effective in improving its competitiveness. If its burgers are made tastier, more people will choose them over Burger King and it will make more profits because it will have more customers. Productivity is also important since it makes the company run smoothly.

Mark awarded	Reasons

Activity 4: Improve an answer

Look at the question below:

> The World Wildlife Fund (WWF) is a pressure group campaigning to prevent the extinction of bluefin tuna. Fishermen use nets which not only catch tuna but other animals such as dolphins. The WWF wants fishermen to use different methods which would reduce the amount of tuna caught and stop other marine animals from being killed.
>
> In response to the work of the WWF, retailers of tuna can respond in one of the following two ways:
>
> **Option 1:** Do nothing.   **Option 2:** Sell only tuna caught in an environmentally friendly way.
>
> In your opinion which one of these two options should retailers adopt, and why? (6 marks)

The response below gained just 2 out of 6 marks. Your task is to improve this response to the point where it scores at least 4 marks. Then, in the box provided, explain briefly why your response improves on that of the student.

Student A:

I would do nothing because not that many people care about how tuna is caught.

Remember

To get 4 marks you need to:

- decide which option is best
- develop that option with linked sentences, justifying your choice
- include at least one reason/cause/consequence
- refer to the tuna/fishing context.

You can refer to both options in your answer – but you do not need to do this. Demonstrating the skills of analysis are more important in this type of question.

Your answer: (this has been started for you)

> The best choice a retailer could make is to do nothing. This is because: ....
>
> ....
>
> ....
>
> ....

Reasons why this is an improvement:

....

....

....

....

Activity 5: Build an answer

Now try to do the same thing by giving the argument from the other perspective.

The World Wildlife Fund (WWF) is a pressure group campaigning to prevent the extinction of bluefin tuna. Fishermen use nets which not only catch tuna but other animals such as dolphins. The WWF wants fishermen to use different methods which would reduce the amount of tuna caught and stop other marine animals from being killed.

In response to the work of the WWF, retailers of tuna can respond in one of the following two ways:

Option 1: *Do nothing.*   **Option 2:** *Sell only tuna caught in an environmentally friendly way.*

In your opinion which one of these two options should retailers adopt, and why? (6 marks)

Remember

You can answer this type of question by considering either of the options. Alternatively, you could consider both options in your answer. For this question you could focus on the 'do nothing' option **OR** the 'selling only tuna caught in an environmentally friendly way' option **OR** both – it's up to you! So long as you can justify your choice.

The best choice a retailer could make is to only sell tuna caught in an environmentally friendly way.

This is because ....

....

....

....

....

....

....

....

....

....

....

....

....

....

Hint

Thinking about **why** one thing is better than another thing is a good revision strategy. You have to think, and using these skills will get you more marks!

Activity 1: Understanding the exam question

Read the following question:

> Two ways in which lorry companies can be helped when the economy is in recession are to:
>
> ⊙ reduce the tax on fuel
>
> ⊙ reduce interest rates.
>
> In your opinion, which of these two ways will be most effective in helping a lorry company during a recession? Justify your answer.   *(6 marks)*

The best way to build your answer to this type of question is to use the same techniques as for 'Explain' questions (see page 39). Building an answer using linking words or phrases, such as 'because' and 'this will mean' will help you to structure your ideas and provide analysis through giving reasons/causes/consequences.

In the space below there is an incomplete answer. Use the linking words and phrases to complete the answer.

| therefore | as a result | will mean that |

> Lower interest rates will most benefit lorry companies. Lower interest rates ....
>
> ....the companies have lower fixed costs. ....the
>
> companies' total costs will fall and ....
>
> profits may be higher.

Activity 2: Build an answer

Look at the three student responses in the table below. The first part of each answer is highlighted in yellow and the second part is highlighted in blue.

Indicate with a tick in the final column whether the second part is linked to the first part of the answer. If it is not, use a cross .

	Response	Linked?
A	Interest rates are the amount charged by banks when individuals or businesses borrow money. Lower interest rates will help lorry businesses to reduce fixed costs.	
B	Lower interest rates will help lorry companies, especially if the business has loans on which it pays interest. This will help to reduce fixed costs, but only of those businesses which have loans.	
C	Lower taxes on fuel will certainly help lorry companies by reducing their variable costs. This will be a good thing for the business.	

Activity 3: Using the mark scheme

Look at the question again:

> Two ways in which lorry businesses can be helped when the economy is in recession are to:
>
> - reduce the tax on fuel
> - reduce interest rates.
>
> In your opinion, which of these two ways will be most effective in helping a lorry company during recession? Justify your answer.　　　(6 marks)

Now look at the mark scheme to this question:

Marks	Description
1	Simple judgement given about which is the best method. Either no further development is offered, or very simplistic development.
2	Judgment is given with some simple development.
3	Judgement is given on one or both ways with some development/support, which includes at least one reason/cause/consequence, etc.
4	A judgement is given on one or both ways with some development/support, which includes at least one reason/cause consequence, etc. Answer will refer to context of lorry businesses.

Use the mark scheme to mark the answer below. Place your score in the box below, explaining your reasons.

Student A:

The thing that will be most effective in helping a lorry business during recession will be to reduce the tax on fuel. As fuel is the main variable cost used by a transport business, so a cut in tax will mean lower costs. This will mean that the business will make more profit. Lower interest rates will also help as this will help to reduce costs.

Mark awarded	Reasons

Activity 4: Improve an answer

You will now look at an actual student response for the question below.

> *Pollution and the use of non-renewable resources are two drawbacks of economic growth.*
>
> *Which of these do you think is most serious and why?* (6 marks)

Student A:

The most serious effect is pollution. This is because pollution affects everybody and can cause externalities.

This response gained just 2 marks out of 6. Your task is to improve this response to the point where it scores at least 4 marks. Then, in the box provided below, explain briefly why your response improves on that of the student.

Your answer: (this has been started for you)

The most serious drawback of economic growth is pollution. This is because:

....

....

....

....

....

....

....

Remember

To get 4 marks you need to:

o make a decision

o give at least one developed explanation containing linked statements which help to justify your decision

o use appropriate business concepts and terms.

You can refer to both options in your answer – but you do not need to do this. Demonstrating the skills of analysis are more important in this type of question.

Reasons why this is an improvement:

....

....

....

....

....

Activity 5: Build an answer

Now try to do the same thing by giving the argument from the other perspective.

Pollution and the use of non-renewable resources are two drawbacks of economic growth.

Which of these do you think is most serious and why? (6 marks)

Remember

You can answer this type of question by considering either of the options. Alternatively, you could consider both options in your answer. For this question you could focus on pollution **OR** non-renewable resources **OR** both – it's up to you! So long as you can justify your choice.

The most serious drawback of economic growth is the use of non-renewable resources.

This is because ....

....

....

....

....

....

....

....

....

....

....

....

....

....

....

Hint

Thinking about **why** something is better than something else is a good revision strategy. You have to think, and using these skills will get you more marks!

Introduction to 'Discuss' questions

Questions starting with the word 'discuss' will be mostly found in **Section C** of the exam paper, but could also be in Section B. They are usually worth 6 marks and they are linked to a case study at the start of the section. Most 'Discuss' questions are about a problem/opportunity/benefit faced by a business or an economy.

> **Note:** This type of question may not appear on every question paper. This is provided as guidance for when such a question does appear!

Any student aiming to achieve a good grade should be able to score at least 3 marks on this type of question. To get 3 marks you need to write and explain up to **two** factors relating to why that issue might be important to the business or economy in question. You **will also** need to put a value on one of the issues you have written about or think about a different point of view. This is called **adding balance** to your answer.

To reach 4 marks you need to make sure you apply your answer to the business mentioned in the question.

> **Hint**
>
> Try and make your balance stand out by putting it in a separate paragraph at the end of your answer. If you can apply your answer to the business you could even get 4 marks!

A typical question

Discuss the importance of developing new products in allowing a company like Pepsi to increase its competitiveness. (6 marks)

A 4-mark answer

Having new flavours of colas will make Pepsi more attractive to its customers because they will want to try the new flavours. This means they will buy more and the company will make more profit. New products will also improve Pepsi's brand and allow it to do better than Coca-Cola, stealing its customers.

However, developing new colas is expensive and risky and if they don't taste nice it can actually damage Pepsi rather than benefit it.

Why does this answer gain 4 marks?

'Discuss' questions are marked using a 'levels of response' mark scheme. You need to aim for your answer to get into level 2 (3–4 marks).

Level/ Mark	Descriptor
Level 2 3–4 marks	Two reasons are given with some development of each. A judgement/point is given at the lower end of the level with some development/support, which includes at least one cause/consequence, etc., for each benefit.
	At the top of the level this analysis will be relevant and linked to the judgement/point made and there may be some reference to the context.

The answer above scored 4 marks (top level 2) because **two** benefits of developing new products were mentioned and explained (the first is highlighted in red and the second in yellow). There was also some balance since the costs and risk of developing new products were mentioned, therefore a consequence was written about. This balance was made clear to the examiner since it was put in a separate paragraph. The answer was also applied to Pepsi/Coca-Cola/cola drinks.

Activity 1: Understanding the exam question

In 'Discuss' questions you need to be **analytical** and **evaluative**. This involves making a judgement about problems/opportunities/benefits faced by a company and offering some support.

Look at the question below:

> *Affinity is a small publishing company that produces guide books containing short walks for parents with small children and prams.*
> *Discuss the benefits to Affinity of improved motivation of its employees.*   (6 marks)

On the left-hand side of the table below, there are two reasons why improved motivation will benefit Affinity. On the right-hand side of the table, develop each benefit using two sentences. This is what you will need to do in the first paragraph of your answer.

Benefit	Explanation
Better quality of products because:	Sentence 1:
	Sentence 2:
Higher profits because:	Sentence 1:
	Sentence 2:

After you have written your first paragraph, you need to write a second paragraph that contains some balance or places a value on one of the reasons you have identified. For example, if you think better quality will lead to more sales then how many more sales will this create? A very large amount, a reasonable amount or hardly any change in sales at all? This is what is meant by putting a value on points you make.

Using the table below, tick a box and choose which of the two benefits is most important. Then write a sentence below explaining your choice.

Benefit of improved employee motivation	Most important
Better quality of products	
Higher profits	
Explain why the benefit you have chosen is most important:	

By following this structure your answer should be able to gain 3 marks. If you apply your answer to the business in the question you may be able to reach 4 marks. Go back and have a look at your sentences of explanation. Did you use the words 'Affinity', 'guide books', 'walks', etc.?

Activity 2: Using the mark scheme

Look at the question below:

Discuss the importance of promotion as a method of increasing the motivation of workers at KFC. (6 marks)

Now look at the mark scheme for this question:

Level/Mark	Descriptor
Level 2 3–4 marks	Reference as to why promotion is important is given with development. A judgement/point is given at the lower level with some development/support which includes one reason/cause/consequence.

At the top of this level answers will be relevant and linked to the judgement/point made and there may be some reference to the context. |

Use the mark scheme to mark the student answer provided below, placing your score in the box below the answer:

Student A:

Promotion is a very important way of increasing motivation at KFC. The job at KFC is a hard one and at lunch time the restaurants are really busy. Workers who do well and can cope with the stress will be boosted by promotion and work harder. Promotion also makes a worker feel important and if you feel important you will like working for KFC. Therefore you won't leave and go and work in Burger King instead. KFC won't need to spend as much on training.

Promotion can be important in motivating people, but working at KFC is not a nice job because it's really greasy and smelly. Therefore most workers are only doing it for the money.

Mark awarded = [   ] /6

With a highlighter pen, go back to the student answer above and highlight all the places where the answer has been applied to KFC. Use the answers in the back of the book to check if you found them in all the right places.

Activity 3: Improve an answer

Look at the question below:

> *Discuss the benefits to BMW of improving its productivity.* (6 marks)

Student A:

If BMW improve its productivity it will be able to make more. By making more products, it will have more to sell. This means it can make more money. Improving productivity also means that the factory is better organised and less mistakes are going to be made.

Examiner's comments:

There is only one paragraph to this answer. The student has considered two reasons why increased productivity could benefit the business and the first reason highlighted in red is more developed than the second highlighted in yellow. The main problem with this answer is that there is no 'discussion'. The student has actually answered the following question: '**Explain** two benefits to a business of improving productivity'.

The command word 'discuss' means you need to add balance or place a value on the points you have made. Balance could be added in a second paragraph to make it clear to the examiner. The answer is not applied to BMW or cars, etc., so it also lacks context. Due to the lack of any balance, the answer cannot get out of level 1, therefore the answer scores 2/6 marks.

The table below lists several ways in which the answer could be improved. Place a tick next to the things which you think the student needs to do to improve their answer so that it gains 4 marks. The first one has been done for you.

Improvement	Yes	No
More benefits of improving productivity		✓
Needs more than one paragraph		
Needs balance		
Needs more use of context		
Needs more explanation of each benefit		

Activity 4: Write an answer

Read the case study and then look at the question below:

> Poundland is a chain of discount stores that was set up in 1990. Everything sold in its stores is priced at £1. It sells everything from binoculars to bread, but the selling price is always the same. During the recession, the number of people shopping in Poundland increased. Retail experts believe this is because people were attracted by its simple pricing strategy of selling everything for £1.
>
> *Discuss the importance of advertising in allowing Poundland to improve its profits.*
>
> *(6 marks)*

You need to remember the following things when writing an answer to this 'Discuss' question:

- You should aim to write **three** paragraphs.

- The first paragraph might explain why advertising is important in allowing Poundland to improve its profits.

- The second paragraph might explain why a different factor may be important in allowing Poundland to improve its profits, e.g. low prices, choice of products, etc.

- In the final paragraph you need to make a choice between advertising and your second factor. You also need to explain your choice and its importance in allowing Poundland to increase its profits.

- Your answer must be applied to Poundland.

 On a separate piece of paper write an answer to this question. Give yourself no longer than six minutes to do this and it would be a good idea to divide this time up into two minutes for each of the three paragraphs. Remember your aim is to try and get at least 3 marks.

You or a friend can now mark the answer using the mark scheme on page 93 at the back of the book.

Activity 1: Understanding the exam question

In 'Discuss' questions you need to be **analytical** and **evaluative**. This involves making a judgement about problems/opportunities/benefits faced by a company and offering some support. Look at the question below:

> *When a business has a market share of 25% it can be classed as a monopoly. Microsoft has a monopoly position in the market for computer operating systems.*
>
> *Discuss the view that monopoly is always bad for consumers.*　　　　(6 marks)

As a first step to tackling this question, first identify two advantages and two disadvantages that a monopoly may have for consumers.

The table below shows some of the advantages and disadvantages of monopolies for consumers. Decide on the importance of each. Place a tick in the table next to each benefit to highlight how important this effect is for consumers (1 = not important, 5 = most important).

Note: this will help you to decide what your answer will be.

Disadvantages	1	2	3	4	5
Can charge high prices as no competition to worry about.					
Poor quality customer service as no competition to worry about.					
Poor quality products as no competition to worry about.					
Advantages	**1**	**2**	**3**	**4**	**5**
The monopoly is a big business and can therefore get economies of scale.					
As it produces on a large scale it can charge lower prices.					
Big businesses like monopolies make large profits and can use these to make new, exciting products.					

Now choose the most important effect and one which you have ranked as less important, and fill in the table below explaining why you made that decision.

Most important effect of monopoly on consumers is...	This is because...

60

By following this structure your answer should be able to gain 3 marks. If you word your answer around the type of business in the question you may be able to reach 4 marks. Go back and have a look at your sentences of explanation.

Hint

Try to show some original thinking in this section!

Activity 2: Using the mark scheme

Look at the question below:

> All businesses use the marketing mix – product, price, promotion and place – to help achieve their aims.
>
> Discuss the importance of promotion as a method of increasing the sales at KFC.   (6 marks)

Now look at the mark scheme for this question:

Level/ Mark	Descriptor
Level 2 3–4 marks	Reference as to why promotion is important is given with development. A judgement/point is given at the lower level with some development/support which includes one reason/cause/consequence. At the top of this level answers will be relevant and linked to the judgement/point made and there may be some reference to the context.

Use the mark scheme to mark the student answer provided below, placing your score in the box below the answer.

Student A:

Promotion is a very important way of increasing sales at KFC. The market is very competitive and so KFC needs to make sure its customers are aware of its products. It will also have to offer promotions and special offers to ensure it competes with McDonald's 'Happy Meals', for example.

Promotion is very important for KFC. It is the most important part of the marketing mix by far. If KFC does not get its promotion right, it may struggle.

Mark awarded = [   ] /6   How might this answer be improved?

Improvement	Tick
Provide a definition of 'promotion'	
Give one other factor that may be important for KFC to increase sales	
Provide more detailed explanations of points	
Needs more linking sentences	
Provide balance	
Compare promotion to other elements of the marketing mix	

Activity 3: Improve an answer

Look at the question below:

> *Discuss the benefits to BMW of increasing in size.* (6 marks)

Student A:

If BMW increases in size it means it will be selling more cars. This will mean more sales revenue and therefore more profit. Also, if it is a bigger company it will have a bigger market share.

Hint

For a 'Discuss' question you must provide **different** reasons.

'Explain' questions require linked statements, not 'Discuss' ones.

Examiner's comments:

There is only one paragraph to this answer. The student has considered two reasons why increased size could benefit the business. The first reason – highlighted in red – is more developed than the second – highlighted in yellow.

The main problem with this answer is that there is no 'discussion'. The student has actually answered the following question: '**Explain** two benefits to BMW of increasing in size'. The command word 'discuss' means you need to add balance; this should be done in a second paragraph to make it clear to the examiner.

The answer is applied to BMW or cars, etc., so it does have context.

Due to the lack of any balance the answer scores 3 marks.

Look at the table below. The table lists several ways in which the answer could be improved. Place a tick next to the things which you think the student needs to do to improve their answer so that it gains 4 marks. The first one has been done for you.

Improvement	Yes	No
More benefits of increasing in size		✓
Needs more than one paragraph		
Needs balance		
Needs more use of context		
Needs more explanation of each benefit		

Activity 4: Write an answer

Read the evidence and then look at the question below:

NEW RULES TO REDUCE BINGE DRINKING

Pubs, bars and shops face new rules aimed at reducing binge drinking.
The government is worried about the cost of alcohol-related illness and the
negative externalities associated with binge drinking.

One of the reasons given for the rise in binge drinking is the low price of alcohol.
Some supermarkets are charging as little as 22p a can for their own brand beer.
Many pubs run special offers including 2 for 1, and happy hours. In addition,
the fact that incomes are rising means more people can afford to buy alcohol.

Discuss the effectiveness of high taxes as the best way to reduce binge drinking. (6 marks)

You need to remember the following things when writing an answer to this
'Discuss' question:

- You need to write in **three** paragraphs.

- The first paragraph should explain why taxation might be useful in dealing with
  binge drinking.

- The second paragraph should explain why a different factor may be important
  in dealing with binge drinking.

- In the final paragraph you need to make a choice between taxation and the
  other method you have identified. You then need to give a reason why you
  made that choice.

- Your answer must be applied to binge drinking.

 On a separate piece of paper, write an answer to this question. Give yourself no
longer than six minutes to do this and it would be a good idea to divide this time up
into two minutes for each of the three paragraphs.

You or a friend can now mark the answer using the mark scheme on page 93 at the back of
the book.

Introduction to 'Assess' questions

Questions starting with the word 'assess' typically appear in **Sections B and C** of the exam paper.

'Assess' questions, worth 8 marks, will be linked to a business or economic context. Most refer to a particular problem/benefit/opportunity faced by a business or an economy. To answer the question you have to offer a **balanced** answer and/or attach some value to the points you are making. You need to show your ability to 'weigh up' an issue and make a judgement about how important or significant it is.

Note: 8-mark questions which use the command word 'evaluate' require the same approach as the 'assess' questions.

How will I be marked?

This question is worth 8 marks. Any student who wishes to achieve a good grade should aim to get at least 4 or 5 marks on this type of question.

To get this you need to:

○ explain at least two points given

○ make sure at least one of the points is developed

○ provide some balance in your response for 5 marks

○ use appropriate business and economic terms

○ organise your answer into paragraphs.

Hint

In your answer, think about using the phrase 'it depends'. Explain briefly that the decisions you arrive at in your response often **depend** on certain factors or assumptions.

Using 'it depends' in your conclusion will help you avoid providing responses which tend to repeat what you have already said.

The first paragraph should explain why the issue highlighted in the question is important.
The second paragraph will explain why the issue might be more or less important or give an alternative viewpoint.
The final paragraph contains a judgement as to which of the two issues is the most important and why. Consider whether the 'it depends' rule can be used.

A typical question

Princess Yachts International plc sells 15% of its yachts to the USA.

Assess the effects a strong pound might have on Princess Yachts plc's profits. (8 marks)

An 5-mark answer

A strong pound will reduce the cost of importing materials to make its boats from abroad. This will help reduce its costs and so improve its profits. This will help if the business has to import lots of its materials. As Princess Yachts make luxury boats it is likely that it does need to import lots. Therefore the strong pound will help.

Good use of terms which show **understanding**.

However, as Princess Yachts exports some of its boats, this might mean that fewer foreign customers will be able to afford it as the strong pound means that foreign currencies are weaker.

Student offers simple **balance** here.

Why does this response gain 5 marks?

This response gets 5 marks because the student makes at least two points. They state that the strong pound will benefit Princess Yachts since imports will be cheaper as a result. They offer development of this by using business terms such as 'costs' and 'profit'.

The response offers a simple **balance** answer which explains that the strong pound might cause some problems. It is clear to the examiner that the second paragraph provides balance as it begins with the word, 'However'.

Hint

A conclusion would have helped the student bring the response to a close.

The student clearly understands that a strong pound will benefit an importer, and then shows a clear grasp of how this might impact on profit. This is required by the question.

Activity 1: Understanding the exam question

'Assess' questions require you to show **balance** and/or place a value on points you make. For each of the questions below you are provided with an argument. Your task is to provide an opposing argument and place a value on the argument.

Remember

A good way of showing balance is to begin a paragraph with 'however'.

Question 1:

Sony is a large Japanese electronic company. It manufactures televisions, DVD players and music players. Due to competition, Sony has had to close several factories, making workers unemployed.

Assess the impact of job losses on the motivation of the remaining Sony employees.

(8 marks)

Argument	Balancing argument
With so many Sony workers losing their jobs, the workers that remain in the business will be scared of losing their jobs as well. This will mean that the remaining workers will be demotivated because they are no longer having their security needs met.	However, motivation does not have to go down for all Sony employees that are still employed. For example, ... The overall impact of job losses depends on ....

Question 2:

First Great Western is a train operating company that run trains in the south-west of England and Wales. Its drivers are rewarded with a good salary and a range of fringe benefits, including a number of free rail tickets for their families and a free uniform.

Assess the likely importance of fringe benefits in allowing First Great Western to recruit more staff.

(8 marks)

Argument	Balancing argument
Fringe benefits will make a worker feel more valued by a business and will attract people to work for First Great Western. This is because the free uniform and rail tickets mean that the worker and his/her family will not have to spend their own money on these items. Therefore it is similar to boosting the workers' pay.	However, if First Great Western only give one or two free journeys then .... However, the overall importance of fringe benefits in recruiting more staff depends on ....

Now attempt this question, but this time the answer provides less structure.

Question 3:

British Gas supplies both gas and electricity to businesses and consumers in the UK.

Assess the importance of good customer service in allowing British Gas to improve its competitiveness. *(8 marks)*

Argument	Balancing argument
Good customer service will make British Gas more attractive to potential customers. This is because, if their complaints are dealt with properly and any problems sorted out quickly, more customers are likely to be attracted to the firm and fewer existing customers will leave. This will boost British Gas' competitive advantage.	However, ... But this depends on ....

Activity 2: How do I use the 'it depends' rule?

In the previous activity we looked at how to bring balance into an answer. In this activity we are going to look at another important way of dealing with 'Assess' or 'Evaluate' questions, and that is to use the 'it depends' rule.

To gain 5 marks or more you will need to show some balance in your answer. One way you can show balance is by using something called the 'it depends' rule. For example:

Eating crisps is bad for your health.

This is a statement, but by using the 'it depends' rule it can be improved to score more marks. Look at this improved response:

Eating crisps is bad for your health, but it depends on how often you eat crisps and what the saturated fat content of the crisps is. If you eat crisps that are baked rather than fried and only eat them once a week, there will be hardly any affect on your health.

Remember
Try to show some original thinking. Don't simply repeat what you have already said. Using the phrase 'it depends' will help you do this.

For each of the following responses, identify and explain one factor on which it will depend.

1. *The most effective way for the business to improve its profitability is to reduce its costs.*

   However, whether this is a success will depend on ....

   ....

   ....

2. *The most important element of the marketing mix is low prices. This is because, when consumer confidence is poor, having low prices will increase demand.*

   However, the importance of low prices depends on ....

   ....

   ....

3. *Increasing prices is one important way in which a business could increase profits.*

   However, whether this works or not will depend on ....

   ....

   ....

   ....

Remember
Don't just use 'it depends' in your conclusion. You need to be thinking about this throughout your answer.

Activity 3: Understanding the mark scheme

Look at the three student responses below and decide which one is the best.

The responses are based on the following question:

Assess the impact of using loans as a method of financing the growth of a business.

(8 marks)

Student A:

Using loans to finance the growth of a business can increase the chance of the business failing. This is because interest has to be paid on a loan. This interest is an extra cost to the business which will reduce its profits. If interest rates rise, the costs of the firm could increase a lot, although this would depend on how high interest rates are increased by and the size of the loan taken out in the first place.

Student B:

Loans can be used by a business to expand. However, loans are expensive because interest has to be paid. This interest adds to the costs of the firm and reduces its profits. This is a big problem when interest rates go up.

Student C:

Bank loans are also called loan capital. This is an external source of finance. In order to get a loan, the business has to submit a business plan. If the bank likes the business plan it will offer a loan to the business. The interest rate on the loan is calculated according to how risky the business is to the bank. If the business is high risk, they may not get a loan or, if they do, the interest paid will be much higher. Paying interest on loans can be quite expensive.

> **Hint**
> The longest answer is not always the best answer.

I think the best response is: Student ....
Two reasons why this is best are:
1. ....
....
....
2. ....
....
....

> **Remember**
> Show some original thinking in your conclusion. Don't simply repeat what you have already said.

Activity 4: Write an answer

Look at the case study and question below:

> The Saltash Toy Box is a small independent retailer located in Cornwall. It cannot compete on price with larger retailers such as ToysRUs, but instead focuses on customer service and allowing children to play with toys, in store, before parents buy them.
>
> Despite its efforts to compete, however, sales at the store remained low. The owner decided to change the focus of the business. In 2010, the Saltash Toy Box closed its only retail store and instead decided to focus on catalogues and its website as a way of making sales. It believed this would boost the company's profits and increase the productivity of its two staff.
>
> *Assess the effect of the change of focus on the competitiveness of the Saltash Toy Box.*
>
> *(8 marks)*

Remember

When a question asks you to 'assess' you must offer some balance. This could be done by thinking about whether or not the change of focus will be successful or whether there are better ways for the Saltash Toy Box to improve its competitiveness.

You need to remember the following things when writing an answer to this 'Assess' question:

- You need to write at least **three** paragraphs.

- The first paragraph should explain how the change in focus could improve the competitiveness of the Saltash Toy Box.

- The second paragraph should explain why a different change could have improved the competitiveness of the Saltash Toy Box to a greater/lesser extent.

- The third paragraph should contain balance using the 'it depends' rule. Think about the things that will make selling toys by the Internet/catalogues more or less successful.

- Your answer must be applied to the Saltash Toy Box and toy retailing.

 On a separate piece of paper write an answer to this question.
Give yourself no longer than eight minutes to do this.

You or a friend can now mark the answer using the mark scheme on page 94 at the back of the book.

Activity 1: Understanding the exam question

'Assess' questions need you to show **balance** and/or place a value on points you make. For each of the questions below you are provided with an argument. Your task is to provide an opposing argument and place a value on the argument.

Question 1:

Assess the effect of lower interest rates on the UK economy. (8 marks)

Argument	Balancing argument
Lower interest might mean that consumers spend more of their income. This is because mortgage repayments will be lower and they will have more disposable income. This will benefit businesses in the economy as they are likely to receive higher sales. However, the size of the effect will depend on how low interest rates are and how much extra disposable income people have.	*However, lower interest rates will not be a good thing for people with savings.* *This is because* .... *The overall impact of lower interest rates depends on* ....

Question 2:

Businesses such as Microsoft and Sky can be described as monopolies. Assess the impact of monopolies on consumers in the UK. (8 marks)

Argument	Balancing argument
Monopolies can be harmful for consumers. By having no real competition, monopolies can charge very high prices. Consumers have to pay these prices as there are no other companies selling the product. The size of the effect on consumers does depend on how strong the monopoly is – people do not have to buy Sky, for example.	*However, monopolies can have some benefits for consumers.* *For example,* .... *However, the overall impact of monopolies on consumers* *depends on* ....

Remember

A good way of showing balance is to begin a paragraph with 'however'.

Now attempt this question, but this time the answer provides less structure.

Question 3:

Assess the importance of cash flow as a reason for business failure. (8 marks)

Argument	Balancing argument
Without strong cash flow a business will struggle. Cash is needed to pay workers and suppliers. If suppliers are not paid then the business will find that it cannot get hold of materials to produce its product. As a result it may not be able to generate the revenue needed to cover costs. So, cash flow is an important cause of business failure. The importance of cash flow will vary according to the business. The more regular cash flow is the easier it is to manage.	*However,* .... *Whether this is more important than cash flow depends on* ....

Activity 2: How do I use the 'it depends' rule?

In the previous activity we looked at how to bring balance into an answer. In this activity we are going to look at another important way of dealing with 'Assess' or 'Evaluate' questions, and that is to use the 'it depends' rule.

To gain 5 marks or more you will need to show some balance in your answer. One way you can show balance is by using the idea of 'it depends'. For example:

Charging a higher price will be good for a business as it means it will receive more revenue. This is a decent enough statement and shows some fair understanding: higher price = higher revenue. However, by thinking about what it might depend upon, a better answer can be arrived at. Look at the following response:

Student A:

Charging a higher price will be good for a business as it means it will receive more revenue. However, if the business has lots of competitors then charging a high price might be harmful. Whether it works or not depends on the amount of competition.

> **Remember**
> Try to show some original thinking. Don't simply repeat what you have already said. 'It depends' will help you do this.

For each of the following responses, identify and explain one factor on which it will depend.

1. *The most effective way for the government to reduce relative poverty in the UK is to increase state benefits. However, whether this is a success will depend on* ....

   ....

   ....

   ....

2. *Whether high levels of economic growth will be good for the economy depends on* ....

   ....

   ....

   ....

3. *Reducing wages for its workers is one important way in which a business could increase profits. However, whether this works or not will depend on* ....

   ....

   ....

   ....

> **Remember**
> Don't just use 'it depends' in your conclusion. You need to be thinking about this throughout your answer.

Activity 3: Understanding the mark scheme

Look at the three student responses below and decide which one is the best.

The responses are based on the following question:

> Assess the impact of a rise in interest rates on UK consumers. (8 marks)

Student A:

Higher interest rates will mean that consumers have less money to spend. This is because mortgage payments will increase and so they will be left with less disposable income. Higher interest rates will therefore be bad for consumers.

Student B:

Higher interest rates will mean that savers have more money from interest. They will be able to spend more money and therefore have a higher standard of living. This is a good thing. However, how much they benefit will depend on the size of their savings.

Student C:

Interest rates are the reward for savings. They can also be charged on loans. Interest rates are set by the Bank of England. A long-term type of loan is a mortgage. Lots of people in the UK have a mortgage. If interest rates increase then people will have less money to spend on goods and services in the economy. Other businesses may well suffer as a result of the higher interest rates.

> **Hint**
> The longest answer is not always the best answer.

I think the best response is: Student ....

Two reasons why this is best are:

1. ....

....

....

2. ....

....

....

> **Remember**
> Show some original thinking in your conclusion. Don't simply repeat what you have already said.

Activity 4: Write an answer

Look at the question below:

> *Assess the view that profit is the best way to measure the success of a business.* (8 marks)

On a separate piece of paper write an answer to this question.

Remember

When a question asks you to 'assess', you must offer some balance. For this question you need to think why profit is a good measure of success, and then think of how it is not the only measure of success.

Hint

Before attempting this, read your notes from Topic 5.2 on 'How can success be measured?'.

Give yourself no longer than eight minutes to do this.

Use the following checklist to help you plan your response.

Checklist	Tick
I have spent about eight minutes writing my answer.	
I have made a decision about the extent to which profit is the best measure of success.	
I have given at least one reason why profit is the best measure of success along with a consequence.	
I have explained one other possible measure of success and have given at least one reason/cause/consequence why these other measures might be an effective measure of success.	
I have said how important they are and why.	
I have used the 'it depends' rule – for example, which measure is dependent on how the business defines 'success'.	
I have written a conclusion which does not just re-state the question.	

You or a friend can now mark the answer using the mark scheme on page 94 at the back of the book.

Introduction to 'Using your knowledge of economics/business, assess...' questions

The final question on the exam paper will often start with the phrase 'Using your knowledge of economics/business, assess...'. The question will be linked to a case study at the start of Section C and will be worth 10 marks.

This style of question wants you to consider how important a problem/opportunity/benefit is to a business/economy. Any student wishing to achieve a good grade should aim to score at least 6 marks on this type of question.

How will I be marked?

To get 6 marks you need to:

- Write and explain why the problem/benefit/opportunity is important, giving up to **two** separate reasons/causes/consequences.

- You then need to think of a totally different factor to the one mentioned in the question and suggest why this is more/less important. This is called adding balance to your answer.

- You could also place a value on the problem/opportunity/benefit you have talked about.

Hint

Make your balance stand out by putting it in a separate paragraph, starting with the word 'however'. This will increase the chances of your answer scoring 6 marks.

A typical question

Using your knowledge of business, assess the importance of good communication to a company such as Affinity. (10 marks)

A 6-mark answer

Good communication is really important to Affinity. This is because good communication will increase the motivation of workers. They will now have a clear idea of what they need to do, so they will produce more books.

Good communication is also important because it stops mistakes being made, so the quality of the book will go up. This will increase Affinity's profit, because more people will buy a book which is better quality. This is particularly important for a guide book because it has to be accurate and easy to read.

However, good communication is not the only important thing in allowing Affinity to be a success. Things like low prices are also important to its customers as well.

Why does this response gain 6 marks?

'Using your knowledge of economics/business, assess…' questions are marked using a 'levels of response' mark scheme. Your aim is to reach level 2 (5–7 marks).

Level/Mark	Descriptor
Level 2 5–7 marks	Candidates consider the importance of good communication to Affinity and offer two or more reasons/causes/consequences, etc., in support.
	At the middle of the level a judgement/conclusion will be made but with no support and merely re-stating the question.
	At the top of the level candidates may offer at least one other factor to balance out the answer. A judgement/conclusion will be made with some support given although not drawn from the analysis and there may be reference to the context.

The answer on the previous page scored 6 marks (mid-level 2) because:

- The student explained **two** developed reasons why good communication was important using **two** separate paragraphs.

- The student then provided some balance in the third paragraph by suggesting that other factors were more important than good communication such as good marketing and low prices.

Activity 1: Understanding the exam question

In the final question you need to explain why a benefit/opportunity/problem is important to a business using **two** separate reasons/causes/consequences. To reach the top of level 2 you need to provide some balance within your answer. You could do this by examining a different point of view or by placing a value on one or more of the points you have made.

Look at the case study evidence and question below:

In 2008 Pepsi launched its first major product since 1993. Pepsi Raw is a cola drink that is made entirely from natural ingredients, and contains no artificial flavouring or sweeteners. Critics of the new drink argue that Pepsi is using the words 'raw' and 'natural' to make consumers believe that the new cola is a healthy product. Although each bottle contains 25% fewer calories than regular Pepsi-Cola, it still contains more calories and high levels of sugar compared to other healthier drinks.

Using your knowledge of business, assess whether Pepsi is right to use the words 'raw' and 'natural' in relation to its new product. (10 marks)

There are three reasons given in the evidence (A, B, C) why Pepsi might be right in using those words listed in the table below:

Reasons why Pepsi might be right	
A	It is not illegal to use the words 'natural' and 'raw' on packaging.
B	Pepsi Raw has 25% fewer calories than normal Pepsi-Cola.
C	Pepsi Raw only uses natural ingredients.

Use the table below to find the correct explanation for each reason, by writing A, B and C in the correct box. Notice how the linking words have been written in bold text.

Explanation		Linked to reason (A,B,C)
1	**This means that** it is a healthier drink **because** it does not have as many calories. **As a result** using the words raw and natural back up that Pepsi Raw is not as bad for you as other colas.	
2	**This means that** it cannot be wrong for Pepsi to use them. The label will tell the customer exactly how much sugar is in the drink and if they do not read the label, that's not Pepsi's fault.	
3	**This means that** using the words raw and natural is totally accurate. If there is nothing artificial in the drink, then Pepsi are doing nothing wrong and can use those words to describe their cola.	

Use the table below to find the correct balancing statement for each explained reason. Write A, B or C in the correct box. Notice that you should always try and use the word 'however' to highlight to the examiner that you are about to provide some balance to your answer.

Balancing statement		Linked to reason (A,B,C)
1	**However**, using these kinds of words does send out a message that the drink is healthy and a consumer could be misled unless they read the label properly.	
2	**However**, some natural ingredients are not good for you. Sugar is a natural ingredient and is not artificial, but eating lots of sugar will make you fat and rot your teeth.	
3	**However**, having less calories in a drink does not mean that it is healthy. If a regular cola had 1000 calories in a can, and a new cola has 750 calories in a can, the second cola might be healthier but it still has a lot of calories and is still bad for you.	

To answer this question you could write **three** separate paragraphs:

- In paragraph 1 you could pick a reason and then explain it.

- In paragraph 2 you could pick a second reason and then explain it.

- Then in the final paragraph you could provide some balance for both of your reasons.

If you do this whilst wording your answer around the business in the question you will score between 5 and 7 marks.

Look at the case study and question below:

In 2010 Marks & Spencer launched a brand new shirt called FreshMax. The shirt uses technology originally developed for football shirts and is designed to prevent embarrassing sweat patches appearing in hot weather, helping the wearer to stay looking cool and 'sweat free'. The shirts are priced at £50 and are more than twice the price of a normal Marks & Spencer shirt.

Marks & Spencer hopes that innovations such as the FreshMax shirt will help it to compete against supermarkets like Asda and Tesco who sell cheap clothing. Asda can sell a basic man's shirt for as little at £6 – 88% cheaper than the Marks and Spencer FreshMax.

Using your knowledge of business, assess the extent to which innovation will allow Marks & Spencer to increase its profitability.   *(10 marks)*

Now look at the mark scheme for this question:

Level/Mark	Descriptor
Level 2 5-7 marks	Candidates consider the importance of innovation in allowing Marks & Spencer to increase its profits and offer two or more reasons/causes/consequences, etc., in support. At the middle of the level a judgement/conclusion will be made but with no support and merely re-stating the question. At the top of the level candidates may offer at least one other factor to balance out the answer. At the top of the level a judgement/conclusion will be made with some support given although not drawn from the analysis and there may be reference to the context.

Use the mark scheme to mark Student A's answer below, placing your score in the box provided.

Student A:

Innovation is really good for Marks & Spencer. By making shirts where you can't look sweaty they will be able to sell lots to people who have a sweat problem. These people will pay more for this kind of shirt since it will stop them from being embarrassed in meetings. As a result Marks & Spencer's profits will go up.

Marks & Spencer will also have an advantage over the competition since, if everyone knows that Marks & Spencer are selling these kinds of clothes, there might be other exciting clothes available in store like clothes that cannot stain, etc. This means that more people will visit them compared to places like Debenhams and TK Maxx. With more customers profits should again rise.

However, innovation is not the only thing that is important to people. People buy clothes for lots of reasons other than just to avoid looking sweaty.

Mark awarded = [/10]

Use the table below to suggest possible improvements to the answer. Put a tick next to the improvements that you think will allow the answer to score more marks.

Improvements	Tick
Paragraph structure could be better	
The first reason needs more development	
The second reason needs more development	
The conclusion could have more balance	
There should be more use of the Marks & Spencer context	

Activity 3: Write an answer

Look at the case study and question below:

Megabus is a discount bus company owned by Stagecoach plc. The business offers a 'no-frills' bus service between towns and cities in the UK. To travel on a Megabus, customers have to book in advance on the Internet. After making the booking, Megabus sends a text message to the customer's mobile phone and the customer shows this to the driver on boarding the bus. Technology like this allows Megabus to keep its costs down. Lower costs also allow Megabus to offer very low fares; Manchester to London can be as cheap as £5 if booked early enough.

However, some customers have criticised the overall service provided by Megabus. The buses can be old and the on-board facilities poor – the toilet can often be blocked, for example. Breakdowns have also occurred and passengers have complained about a lack of legroom.

Some passengers want Megabus to improve the quality of its service.

Using your knowledge of business, assess which element of the marketing mix is most likely to improve Megabus' ticket sales.   *(10 marks)*

You need to remember the following things when writing an answer to this 'Assess' question:

○ You need to write up to **three** paragraphs.

○ The first paragraph should explain why one element of the marketing mix (price, product, promotion, place) could be important in allowing Megabus to improve its ticket sales.

○ The second paragraph should explain why a different element of the marketing mix (price, product, promotion, place) may be more or less important in allowing Megabus to improve its ticket sales.

○ In the final paragraph you need to make a judgement as to which element of the marketing mix is the most important in allowing Megabus to increase sales of tickets, explaining why.

○ Your answer must be applied to Megabus and buses.

 On a separate piece of paper write an answer to this question. Give yourself no longer than ten minutes to do this. It would be a good idea to divide this time up into three minutes and twenty seconds for each of the three paragraphs.

You or a friend can now mark the answer using the mark scheme on page 95 at the back of the book.

Activity 1: Understanding the exam question

In the final questions you need to explain why a benefit/opportunity/problem is important to a business using **two** separate reasons/causes/consequences. You then need to provide balance by giving both sides of an argument, then placing a value on one or more of the points you have made or by looking at things from a different point of view.

Look at the case study evidence and question below:

BEBO ACQUIRED BY AOL

The social networking business, Bebo, has been acquired by media giant AOL in a takeover deal worth £417 million. AOL is part of the Time Warner group. Bebo was set up by husband and wife duo Michael and Xochi Birch in 2005. The couple will get several hundred million dollars from the takeover deal. AOL say that they think that the large user base of Bebo will help them make more money in the future from selling advertising on Bebo and they see it as a good deal.

Others are not quite so sure. Social networking sites like Bebo, MySpace and DoubleClick are being swallowed up by large media corporations and some have questioned whether they will retain their roots.

Using the evidence and your knowledge of economics and business, assess the extent to which consumers of social networking sites, and employees of a business like Bebo, will be disadvantaged by the takeover. (10 marks)

Below are three disadvantages (A, B, C) for consumers of the takeover explained in the evidence.

Disadvantages for customers	
A	Poor quality service due to lack of competition.
B	There will be a more limited choice of other social networking sites.
C	The new company may become a monopoly.

Use the table below to find the correct explanation for each reason, by writing A, B and C in the correct box. Notice how the linking words have been written in bold text.

Explanation		Linked to reason (A,B,C)
1	**This means that** it will probably charge higher prices **because** it will not have as many competitors. **As a result** consumers may choose to find a new provider and this might be inconvenient.	
2	**This means that** consumers will have to stick with AOL. This is because AOL will control the market and will have the major market share.	
3	**This means that** as AOL has removed a major competitor there is no pressure for it to improve its own service. **Therefore**, as a main competitor has been taken over, consumers may have nowhere else to go.	

Use the table below to find the correct balancing statement for each explained reason. Write A, B or C in the correct box. Notice that you should always try and use the word 'however' to highlight to the examiner that you are about to provide some balance to your answer.

	Explanation	Linked to reason (A,B,C)
1	**However**, there will still be other social networking sites. For example, many people use Facebook, so consumers may end up with a better provider.	
2	**However**, a company like AOL will be unlikely to let the quality of its service become poor. The reason it is taking over businesses is to become the best option for consumers.	
3	**However**, as AOL is hoping to generate advertising revenue from sites like Bebo, it may mean that consumers do not have to pay anything to subscribe.	

To answer this question you could write **three** separate paragraphs:

- In paragraph 1 you could pick a reason and then explain it.

- In paragraph 2 you could pick a second reason and then explain it.

- Then in the final paragraph you could provide some balance for both of your reasons.

If you do this whilst applying your answer to the business in the question you will score between 5 and 7 marks.

Activity 2: Using the mark scheme

Look at the case study and question below:

In recent years China has enjoyed record levels of economic growth. However, in this race for growth, the Chinese government has been accused of sacrificing the environment so as to benefit from rapid economic development.

In one town, clouds of yellow smoke hang in the air as a result of the constant burning of plastic. The workers suffer from the polluted fumes from the fires which melt the plastic. The cause of this pollution is the burning of supermarket bags and food packaging waste, imported from Britain. Pollution of this kind not only affects people living in the area, it can also have lasting effects which can affect future generations.

The Chinese government is under increased pressure to regulate pollution in order to achieve sustainable growth.

Economic growth can lead to problems such as pollution. Using your knowledge of business and economics, assess the case for the Chinese government using regulation to achieve sustainable economic growth. (10 marks)

Now look at the mark scheme for this question:

Level/Mark	Descriptor
Level 2 5-7 marks	Candidates consider the importance of regulation for China in securing sustainable economic growth and offer two or more reasons/causes/consequences, etc., in support. At the middle of the level a judgement/conclusion will be made, but with no support, that merely re-states the question. At the top of the level candidates may offer at least one other factor to balance out the answer. At the top of the level a judgement/conclusion will be made with some support given although not drawn from the analysis and there may be reference to the context.

Use the mark scheme to mark Student A's answer below, placing your score in the box provided:

Student A:

Regulation is an important way that China could achieve this type of growth. Regulation is rules and restrictions placed on businesses. China may regulate the amount of pollution that businesses are allowed to make. This will therefore reduce the amount of pollution and should reduce the negative externalities.

Also, regulation will mean that businesses have to pay for the damage they cause. This will mean they will make changes to how they operate, for example by introducing 'greener' machinery which does not damage the environment.

However, regulation may not work. It may mean that businesses may move to countries where rules are more relaxed.

Mark awarded = [/10]

Use the table below to suggest possible improvements to the answer. Put a tick next to the improvements that you think will allow the answer to score more marks.

Improvements	Tick
Paragraph structure could be better	
The first reason needs more development	
The second reason needs more development	
The conclusion could have more balance	
There should be more use of the context of sustainable economic growth	

Activity 3: Write an answer

Look at the case study and question below:

Greggs PLC the bakers originated in the north-east of England in 1984. It has grown through internal and external means. Greggs has expanded to the rest of the country by taking over other regional bakery chains. By 1994 it had 502 shops across the UK. In 1994 it took over a rival business, Bakers Oven, adding an extra 424 shops.

Greggs wanted the Bakers Oven format because many of its shops had in-store bakeries. Greggs had large central bakeries which delivered its products to local shops.

Year	2004	2005	2006	2007	2008
Operating profit (£m)	44.7	47.1	42.2	47.7	44.3

*Using the evidence and your knowledge of economics and business, assess the extent to which customers **and** shareholders might benefit from the growth of Greggs PLC.*

(10 marks)

You need to remember the following things when writing an answer to this 'assess' question:

- You need to write at least **three** paragraphs.

- The first paragraph should explain one way in which customers will benefit from the growth of Greggs, and the extent to which this will affect them.

- The second paragraph should explain one way in which shareholders will benefit from the growth of Greggs, and the extent to which this will affect shareholders.

- The final paragraph allows you to make a judgement as to which group is most affected. Try to use the 'it depends' rule, since customers and shareholders are likely to be affected differently.

- Your answer must be applied clearly to Greggs.

 On a separate piece of paper write an answer to this question. Give yourself no longer than ten minutes to do this.

Remember
Use the context of Greggs. This will help to make sure you score at least 5 to 7 marks. Can you use any data from the evidence?

You or a friend can now mark the answer using the mark scheme on page 96 at the back of the book.

Page 7

Activity 1: Understanding the exam question
A Bad, B Good, C Good, D Answer, E Bad, F Bad

Activity 2: Build an answer
Salary = a fixed payment per year which is paid monthly.

Page 8

Activity 1: Understanding the exam question
A Bad, B Good, C Good, D Bad, E Answer, F Good

Activity 2: Build an answer
Economies of scale = where average total costs fall when output increases.

Page 10

Activity 1: Using the mark scheme
Student A = 2 marks. Problem: Too long.

Student B = 2 marks.

Page 11

Activity 1: Using the mark scheme
Student A = 2 marks.

1.   making more money (profit)

2.   to increase market share

Student B = 2 marks.

Page 13

Activity 1: Build an answer
Student A = 1 mark. This is because the answer made a simple point about 'ethics' involving doing the right thing. To raise the answer to 2 marks, the student could have added a second sentence that includes an example, such as, 'The Co-op tries to do the right thing because its plastic bags biodegrade and it sells lots of Fairtrade products.' (This might make use of the context given in the case study at the start of a section.)

Page 14

Activity 1: Build an answer
Student A = 1 mark. This is because the answer made a simple point about 'exchange rate' involving the value of a currency. To raise the answer to 2 marks, the student could have added a second sentence that included an example, e.g. 'The exchange rate is how much a currency is worth. For example, £1 will currently buy $1.65 – this is its exchange rate.'

Page 16

Activity 1: Understanding the exam question

A	Size of order delivered on day 8	70 pools
B	Re-order level of stock	40 pools
C	Buffer stock	5 pools
D	Time it takes stock to arrive after re-ordering	5 days

Page 17

Activity 2: Build an answer
Margin of safety = 1000 – 750 = 250 souvenirs.

Margin of safety = Current level of output – Break-even level of output

Page 18

Activity 1: Understanding the exam question
2007(12)–2008(9)
Inflation speeds up from 2% to over 5%.

Lower interest rates which lead to higher consumer spending. This is because loans become more expensive and spending on goods such as cars falls.

2008(9)–2009(7)
Inflation slows from over 5% to just under 2%.

Interest rates increased by the Bank of England. Income from savings falls and consumers have less disposable income. Pressure on prices falls.

Page 19

Activity 2: Understanding the exam question

A = 0 marks. This is because there is no real understanding.

B = 2 marks. This is because there is clear definition and an example drawn from the diagram.

C = 1 mark. This is because they know what is meant by the exchange rate, but do not use an example from the chart.

Page 21

Activity 1: Using the mark scheme
Student A = 2 marks. This is because there is no formula stated and this is asked for in the question. The student has calculated contribution per unit, therefore evidence of 'workings' exist and s/he has provided the correct answer.

Page 22

Activity 2: Build an answer
Write down formula: Profit = total revenue – total costs.

Put numbers into the formula: Revenue = price x quantity sold = £300 x 20 000 consoles = £6,000,000. Total costs = fixed costs + variable costs = £2,400,000 + (£140 x 20,000) = £5,200,000.

Answer in units: £6,000,000 - £5,200,000 = £800,000.

Page 23

Activity 1: Build an answer
£25   insensitive   £25   1000   increased   higher

Page 24

Activity 2: Build an answer
Calculate amount per kg in pounds: €5/1.25 = £4

Multiply the unit price by number of units bought: £4 x 100 = 400

Answer in correct currency: £400

Page 26

Activity 1: Using the mark scheme
Student A = 1 mark. Response provides a list and does not provide any development of any of these points. A list, providing it includes valid suggestions, scores 1 mark. Both of the consumer protection laws listed are valid.

Student B = 2 marks. The response offers a valid suggestion – the Trades Description Act - and provides an example developing the answer.

Student C = 0 marks. The student knows something about consumer protection law, but has not mentioned a specific law. Consumer protection laws do not regulate prices or quality.

Page 27
Activity 2: Understanding the question
A = Not. These are two separate points. The second sentence does not develop the first. This answer scores 1 mark since both sentences are independent of one another.

B = Developed. The point is made and then linked to a second point. The second point then leads into a third linked point. The overall result is 3 marks.

C = Developed. The point of increasing costs is given and then two separate unlinked reasons are given as to why costs might increase. The answer scores 2 marks.

Page 28
Activity 3: Improve an answer
1 = Yes. The definition is not giving an extra mark, so therefore it is wasting the student's time.

2 = No. The student already has enough linked statements in their answer.

3 = Yes. Other than one mention of the word Mars, the student has not applied their answer to the business and product in the question.

4 = No. This is a 3-mark outline question. There is no need for lots of detail.

5 = No. The question is not asking you to do this, and this will not gain the student any extra marks.

Activity 4: Improve an answer
Strengths: The answer is applied to the Snickers context. Provides one strategy plus two linked statements.

Areas for improvement: The answer is too long. The answer could have stopped earlier and the last sentence was not needed.

Page 29
Activity 1: Using the mark scheme
Student A = 1 mark. Response provides a list and does not provide any development of any of these points. A list, providing it includes valid suggestions, scores 1 mark. Several of the suggestions – lower interest rates and investment –are acceptable.

Student B = 2 marks. The response offers a valid suggestion and provides some development of this.

Student C = 0 marks. The response does not answer the question. It offers an accurate definition of unemployment, but this is not needed in an 'outline' question.

Page 30
Activity 2: Understanding the question
A = Not. Response begins with reference to costs, but then goes on to how the business is managed.

B = Developed. Links together the idea of having more employees to the problem of communication. Uses the phrase, 'This will mean that..'

C = Not. Response offers 'evaluation' rather than **explaining** how higher costs may be a problem for the business.

Page 31
Activity 3: Improve an answer
1 = Yes. Definitions are not required in 'outline' questions.

2 = No. The response already includes linked statements.

3 = No. Paragraphs are not necessary in this type of question.

4 = No. This is a 2-mark 'outline' question. There is no need for lots of details.

5 = Yes. This will ensure the 2 marks.

Improved response:
The business will suffer as foreign consumers will face higher prices. Demand will therefore fall.

Activity 4: Improve an answer
Strengths: Provides linked statements. Uses appropriate business and economics terminology.

Weaknesses: Too long – only a 2-mark outline question so needs one point plus development. Has the direction of change the wrong way round – foreign consumers would face lower prices.

Page 33
Activity 1: Using the mark scheme
Student A = 2 marks. There is a point made about how 'Differentiation allows a firm's products to stand out in the market' and this is developed. The student states that this is because the product is now 'seen as being different'. However, there is no use of the Subway context at all. Since the name Subway appears in the question, a 3-mark answer must be applied to this business.

Page 34
Activity 2: Improve an answer
Subway's baguettes   sandwich market   sandwiches   McDonald's   healthy baguettes

Page 35
Activity 3: Write an answer
Question 1 does not mention the name of a business. Therefore 3 marks can be gained by writing up to three unrelated sentences as to how improved worker motivation might benefit a business or two points with some development of one of them. Question 2 **does** mention the name of a business, so without clear reference to Apple and its products or competition, a student will not be able to gain full marks.

Page 36
Activity 1: Using the mark scheme
Student A = 2 marks. A point is made – 'diseconomies of scale' – and some development is provided about the business being more difficult to manage. Improvements needed: more points, and wording the answer around business growth.

Page 37
Activity 2: Improve an answer
bad   more expensive   benefit   cheaper

Page 38
Activity 3: Write an answer
Question 1 does not mention the name of a business. Therefore 3 marks can be gained by writing up to three unrelated sentences as to how low interest rates might benefit a business or two points with some development of one of them. Question 2 does mention the name of a business, so without clear reference to McDonald's and its products or competition, a student will not be able to gain full marks.

Page 40
Activity 1: Understanding the exam question
Benefit 1 linked to sentence 6 and sentence 2:
Allows McDonald's to have better relationships with meat suppliers. This is because meat suppliers will have to deliver on time. As a result, there will be more trust between them and McDonald's.

Benefit 2 linked to sentence 4 and sentence 3:
Reduces McDonald's costs. This is because less space is needed to store frozen burgers. Therefore smaller, cheaper restaurants can be built.

Benefit 3 linked to sentence 5 and sentence 1:
McDonald's cash flow will be improved. This is because less stock of burgers, baps, etc., need to be purchased. Therefore less money is tied up in stocks of burgers.

(Evidence of the McDonald's context is highlighted in yellow.)

Page 41
Activity 2: Using the mark scheme
Student A = 1 mark. This is because a statement is made that strong cash flow prevents Lidl running out of cash. The definition of cash flow at the start of the answer does not generate any extra marks because this question is asking you to 'explain'. To gain an extra mark, a linked sentence needs to be added onto the end of the second sentence – for example, 'As a result Lidl will be able to pay farmers and food manufacturers on time'. The fact that this extra sentence is applied to Lidl would allow the third mark to be awarded, because the answer is now in context.

Page 42
Activity 3: Improve an answer
This is because *people will see them as a caring supermarket who are interested in things other than just profit*. As a result, the Co-op can *steal customers from other supermarkets like Tesco*.

Page 43
Activity 1: Understanding the exam question
Benefit 1 linked to sentence 2 and sentence 3:
The business will be able to gain lower average costs. This is because it is operating on a larger scale. Therefore it can buy each unit more cheaply.

Benefit 2 linked to sentence 5 and sentence 1:
The business will be able to buy in bulk. As a result this will reduce the average cost of making each unit of output. Therefore it will be able to charge lower prices for its product.

Benefit 3 linked to sentence 6 and sentence 4:
The business will be able to charge lower prices for its products. This is because average costs of production will be lower. As a result the business may become more competitive.

Page 44
Activity 2: Using the mark scheme
Student A = 2 marks. This is because the statement is made that trade restrictions will help to maintain employment (1 mark) and that this will lead to higher standard of living (1 mark). There is a clear link between the two statements; this is necessary for an 'explain' question. The definition at the start of the answer does not generate any extra marks because this question is asking you to 'explain'. To move to 3 marks, the answer needs an additional linking statement.

For example, the student could have said that employment would have been increased because customers would be unable to buy foreign imports, and that this would lead to higher incomes and living standards.

Page 45
Activity 3: Improve an answer
This may mean that *its profit margin is reduced*. Because of this *the business may have to increase the prices it charges its customers*.

Page 47
Activity 1: Understanding the exam question
because   Therefore/As a result   As a result/Therefore

Activity 2: Build an answer
A = Not. B = Linked. C = Linked.

Page 48
Activity 3: Using the mark scheme
Student A = 4 marks. The response makes a judgement and is developed. At least one reason has been provided as to why quality is important. The answer is worded around the McDonald's context since the words 'burger' and 'Burger King' are used.

Page 49
Activity 4: Improve an answer
This is because *many consumers do not care about how the tuna is caught. Many consumers are just interested in the price of tuna and whether it tastes nice. If they change the way the tuna is caught, the costs of catching the tuna will increase and so to will the price.*

Reasons: The option has been developed to include linked sentences and includes at least one reason as to why retailers should 'do nothing'. Use of the word 'caught' highlights the use of the fishing context.

Page 50
Activity 5: Build an answer
This is because *some consumers care about the environment and animal rights and are willing to pay more for tuna which is caught in an environmentally friendly way. If a retailer does not stock this kind of tuna they risk losing sales.*

Page 51
Activity 1: Understanding the exam question
will mean that   Therefore   as a result

Activity 2: Build an answer
A = Not. B = Linked. C = Not.

Page 52
Activity 3: Using the mark scheme
Student A = 3 marks. The response makes a decision. Only one reason is provided, but linked statements are provided as part of the explanation. Appropriate business terms and concepts are used.

Page 53
Activity 4: Improve an answer
This is because *pollution affects everybody and can have a big effect on the NHS. Pollution causes health problems like asthma so the government has to pay for the NHS. This means that taxes have to increase and everyone will be worse off.*

Reasons: This is an improvement because the option has been developed to include linked sentences and includes some analysis. For example, the response suggests that if the NHS has to deal with more cases, taxes will need to rise. Hence, pollution is a drawback of economic growth.

Page 54
Activity 5: Build an answer
This is because *once these resources have gone they have gone forever. This means that everyone in the future will not be able to have resources such as oil, copper, tin and gold. Therefore people's standard of living will be worse.*

Page 56
Activity 1: Understanding the exam question
Sentence 1: This will improve Affinity's branding.

Sentence 2: As a result there will be more repeat purchases of the guide books because mothers will be happy with the walks contained in the books so they will buy more guide books for different areas.

Sentence 1: Motivated workers will do more work in the same amount of time.

Sentence 2: This means guide books will be researched and completed quicker, reducing the costs of making a guide book.

Better quality of products most important. This is because if the guide books have mistakes in them, mothers will not buy the books and so Affinity's brand will be damaged. This could cause sales to fall and for the company to make losses.

Page 57
Activity 2: Using the mark scheme
Student A = 4 marks. The two-paragraph structure makes it easy to mark. There are two developed reasons why promotion may be important in the first paragraph and the student has made a judgement and given it some support in the second. There is clear use of the fast-food context throughout the answer. To improve the answer, the student could have provided some balance by noting a disadvantage/con/cost and developed the second paragraph.

Promotion is a very important way of increasing motivation at KFC. The job at KFC is a hard one and at lunch time the restaurants are really busy. Workers who do well and can cope with the stress will be boosted by promotion and work harder. Promotion also makes a worker feel important and if you feel important you will like working for KFC. Therefore you won't leave and go and work in Burger King instead. KFC won't need to spend as much on training.

Promotion can be important in motivating people, but working at KFC is not a nice job because it's really greasy and smelly. Therefore most workers are only doing it for the money.

Page 58
Activity 3: Improve an answer
All four improvements would benefit the answer.

Page 61
Activity 2: Using the mark scheme
Student A = 3 marks. The two-paragraph structure makes it easy to mark. There are two developed reasons why promotion may be important in the first paragraph and the student has made a judgement and given it some simple support in the second. There is some use of the fast-food context in the answer. To improve the answer, the student could have provided some balance by noting a disadvantage/con/cost and developed the second paragraph by explaining why promotion is so important compared to other elements of the marketing mix. It would have also benefited from more linking sentences.

Page 62
Activity 3: Improve an answer
All bar more context would be needed to improve the answer.

Pages 66–67
Activity 1: Understanding the exam question
Question 1: For example, *managers at Sony are unlikely to lose their jobs and some workers will think that now the firm has cut costs, Sony has become more competitive and their jobs are now safe.* The overall impact of job losses depends on *whether or not the remaining employees think that they will lose their job in the future. If they don't it is likely that motivation will increase rather than fall.*

Question 2: However, if First Great Western only give one or two journeys then *the fringe benefit of working for that company will be worth hardly anything and few people will be attracted to work there.* The overall importance of fringe benefits in recruiting more staff depends on *the number of free rail tickets the worker gets. If the worker makes lots of long distance trips by rail, the value of the free rail tickets could be worth thousands of pounds. This will make the fringe benefit much more attractive, causing recruitment to increase by a large amount.*

Question 3: However, *the amount of time a gas customer needs to speak to a customer service department is quite low and other factors such as low prices are much more likely to be important in allowing British Gas to improve their competitiveness.* But this depends on *the degree to which gas customers think that having a good customer service department is an important reason to choose one gas company over another.*

Page 68
Activity 2: How do I use the 'it depends' rule?
1. However, whether this is a success will depend on *whether costs can be reduced without reducing the quality of the product or service it sells, otherwise it will lose customers.*

2. However, the importance of low prices depends on *what kind of product it sells, because if it is really good quality and luxurious, a low price could make the product look rubbish or poor quality.*

3. However, whether this works or not will depend on *whether demand goes down when the price is increased. If demand falls a lot, profits could go down not up.*

Page 69
Activity 3: Understanding the mark scheme
Student A: Explains a clear impact of taking out loans on the business. Uses the 'it depends' rule to show some balance by highlighting that the size of the impact depends on the size of the loan and by how much the interest rate goes up.

Pages 71–72
Activity 1: Understanding the exam question
Question 1: This is because *if interest rates are too low (they are currently just 0.5%) then there is a chance that spending in the economy may increase too much. High levels of consumer spending can lead to higher inflation. This would be a real problem for the government, given its inflation target of 2%.* The overall impact of lower interest rates depends on *how much interest rates change by. A 2% rise will have a greater impact than a 0.5% increase.*

Question 2: For example, *as monopolies are big businesses they often have economies of scale (lower average costs). This means they can buy in bulk and charge customers low prices.*

Smaller businesses cannot do this. The overall impact of monopolies on consumers depends on *which industry it is. If there is no other competition at all – such as water supplies – then the effect could be worse than in an industry where other rivals do exist – such as supermarkets.*

Question 3: However, *there are other reasons for business failure. Poor cash flow may not lead to business failure in the short run. For example, if the business cannot pay suppliers 'up front', then credit terms – 30 days – are often agreed. Poor cash flow may only be a short term problem. A lack of demand is much more of a problem for a business*. Whether this is more important than cash flow depends on *other factors in the business, such as the level of competition which exists.*

Page 73
Activity 2: How do I use the 'it depends' rule?

1. However, whether this is a success will depend on *how much they increase by.*

2. Whether high levels of economic growth will be good for the economy depends on *how quickly the economy grows. If economic growth is too rapid, inflation may well occur. This is very damaging for the economy.*

3. However, whether this works or not will depend on *to what extent workers are demotivated by the pay cut. It may mean that workers become uninterested in the quality of their work and as a result the business ends up with lower sales.*

Page 74
Activity 3: Understanding the mark scheme
Student B: Shows understanding of how interest rates affect consumers. Uses the 'it depends' rule to show some balance. Neither of the other two responses does this.

Pages 78–79
Activity 1: Understanding the exam question
1 = B. 2 = A. 3 = C.
1 = A. 2 = C. 3 = B.

Pages 80–81
Activity 2: Using the mark scheme
Student A = 6 marks. The three-paragraph structure makes it easy to mark. Two reasons why innovation are important have been developed and explained in the first and second paragraphs. The third paragraph provides some balance by saying that there are other things that are important, but the student does not say what these are and as a result the answer remains in the middle of level 2 because there is no support. The answer is in context and, with more balance in the final paragraph, the answer could have scored more than 6 marks.

Pages 83–84
Activity 1: Understanding the exam question
1 = C. 2 = B. 3 = A.
1 = B. 2 = A. 3 = C.

Pages 85–86
Activity 2: Using the mark scheme
Student A = 6 marks. The three-paragraph structure makes it easy to mark. Two reasons why regulation is important have been developed and explained in the first and second paragraphs. Good use of terms is made. The third paragraph provides some balance by saying that regulation might not work, but the student does not really say why. This remains in the middle of level 2 because there is no support for the

balancing argument. The answer is in context and, with more balance in the final paragraph, the answer could have scored more than 6 marks. There should be more use of the context of sustainable economic growth.

Mark schemes for 'Describe' questions (p35)
Question 1:
Indicative content

For 3 marks, the description will make three relevant points associated with improved worker motivation and how it might benefit a business or up to two points with some development of one of them. This may include a definition. Each descriptive strand will clearly show the importance of improved worker motivation to the business. One mark is awarded for the statement of a benefit, with 1 mark for each relevant point.

Possible benefits include:

- Higher levels of profit.

- Higher productivity.

- Improved customer service.

- Enhanced branding.

- Lower unit costs.

Question 2:
Indicative content

For 3 marks, the description will clearly show the importance of the brand to the success of Apple business. Within the answer there will be at least two clearly identifiable strands of description with some development. The answer should be rooted in the Apple/electronics context. Two marks are awarded for each strand of description and 1 mark is awarded for the use of context. One strand can include a definition.

Possible answers include:

- Makes the firm stand out.

- Increases the number of repeat purchases.

- Enables the firm to add value.

- Allows the firm to charge higher prices without the loss of demand.

- Makes it harder for a new firm to set up in competition.

Mark schemes for 'Describe' questions (p38)
Question 1:
Indicative content

For 3 marks, the description will make three relevant points associated with low interest rates and how these might benefit a business or up to two points with some development of one of them. This may include a definition. Each descriptive strand will clearly show the importance of improved worker motivation to the business.

Possible benefits include:

- Lower fixed costs.

- Higher sales due to higher disposable income for consumers.

- Increased consumer confidence.

- Lower unit costs.

Question 2:
Indicative content

For 3 marks, the description will clearly show how a business like McDonald's might measure its success. Within the answer there will be at least two clearly identifiable strands of description with some development. The answer should be rooted in the McDonald's/fast food context. Two marks are awarded for each strand of description and 1 mark is awarded for the use of context. One strand can include a definition.

Possible answers include:

- Higher sales revenue.
- Increased profit.
- Higher market share.
- Social success – e.g. sponsorships in the local community.

Mark schemes for 'Discuss' questions (p59)
Indicative content

The aim here is for candidates to consider the importance of advertising in allowing Poundland to increase its profits. The question asks the candidate to 'discuss', so the candidate must develop some evidence of balance within their answer. This could take the form of considering the drawbacks and costs of advertising and the likely risks of failure/success. Equally the route to evaluation could be achieved by considering other factors which are perhaps more important in allowing profits to increase, e.g. lower prices/improved product range, etc. or that it might depend on what sort of advertising Poundland carried out. The answer should be in the context of a discount retailer such as Poundland.

Reasons why advertising could increase profits:

- Gain more customers.
- Increase market share.
- Improves the brand.

Reasons advertising may not increase profits:

- Expensive.
- Might not work.
- Other retailers may also advertise at the same time.
- There are other ways to increase profitability.

Level	Descriptor
No mark	Non-rewardable material.
Level 1 1-2 marks	One reason as to why advertising could increase Poundland's profits is given with some simple development or two reasons are given with no development of either.

An alternative route to marks in this level is if just a simple judgement or value is given to one benefit. 1 mark can be awarded for no support and 2 if some simple support is offered. The candidate explains one reason why advertising is/is not important using terminology and inter-linkage of ideas. Alternatively, the candidate could identify two reasons, but the explanation is weak. A candidate who only explains one benefit well cannot go beyond 2 marks. Expect to see no reference |

to Poundland and answers linked to a generic business will be in this range. Answers in this level will have demonstrated no evaluative qualities.

| Level 2 3-4 marks | Reference to two reasons is given with some development of each. A judgement/point is given at the lower end of the level with some development/support, which includes at least one cause/consequence, etc. for each benefit.

At the top of the level this analysis will be relevant and linked to the judgement/point made and there may be some reference to the context. At the bottom end of this level the candidate will have explained two reasons why advertising is/is not important using terminology and inter-linkage of ideas. Without any evaluation evident candidates cannot score above 3 marks.

However, if evaluation is implied or is superficial/weak, e.g. 'advertising might not work', the candidate can reach the top of this level. |

| Level 3 5-6 marks | Reference to two benefits is given with development of each. A judgement/point is given with some development which includes at least two causes/consequences, etc. for each reason and may include some comparison between the two.

Answers at the top of this level will refer to the Poundland context. In this level there will be clear evaluation and the candidate will have discussed the importance of advertising new products in allowing Poundland to improve its profitability. Candidates in this level are likely to weigh advertising against other factors such as lower prices, product choice, etc. Answers in this level are likely to refer specifically to Poundland and the kinds of product it sells rather than a generic business. |

Mark schemes for 'Discuss' questions (p63)
Indicative content

The aim here is for candidates to consider the importance of taxation in addressing the problem of binge drinking. The question asks the candidate to 'discuss', so the candidate must develop some evidence of balance within their answer. This could take the form of considering the drawbacks and costs of taxation and the likely risks of failure/success. Equally the route to evaluation could be achieved by considering other factors which are perhaps more important in dealing with the problem, such as regulation and education. The answer should be in the context of binge drinking.

Reasons why taxation might be effective:

- Will make alcohol more expensive.
- Young people have low levels of income.
- Alternative drinks will become relatively cheaper.

Reasons taxation may not be effective:

- Alcohol consumption is not price sensitive.
- Young people will always find a way to purchase alcohol.
- Education is more important.

Level	Descriptor
No mark	Non-rewardable material.
Level 1 1-2 marks	One reason as to why taxation might work is given with some simple development or two reasons are given with no development of either. An alternative route to marks in this level is if just a simple judgement or value is given to one benefit. 1 mark can be awarded for no support and 2 if some simple support is offered.
Level 2 3-4 marks	Reference to two reasons is given with some development of each. A judgement/point is given at the lower end of the level with some development/support, which includes at least one cause/consequence, etc. for each benefit. At the top of the level this analysis will be relevant and linked to the judgement/point made and there may be some reference to the context.
Level 3 5-6 marks	Reference to two benefits is given with development of each. A judgement/point is given with some development which includes at least two causes/consequences, etc. for each reason and may include some comparison between the two. Answers at the top of this level will refer to the alcohol context.

Mark schemes for 'Assess' questions (p70)
Indicative content

The aim here is for candidates to consider whether changing the 'place' element of the marketing mix will improve Saltash Toy Box's competitiveness. The question asks the candidate to 'assess', so the candidate must develop some evidence of balance within the answer. This could take the form of disadvantages which reduce the size of the benefits to Saltash Toy Box of closing down its retail store, or through a consideration of the extent to which it is likely to be a successful strategy.

Benefits of switching to catalogues/Internet:

- Lower costs/overheads.

- Opportunity for lower prices.

- Greater ability to compete on price with ToysRUs.

- Wider market can be targeted rather than just a small town.

- Increased profit margins.

Drawbacks of switching to catalogues/Internet:

- Will still not be able to compete on price with ToysRUs.

- Will lose its reputation for customer service.

- Loss of USP since children cannot now play with toys before purchase.

- Could lower profits.

- Damage to the brand/loss of local custom.

It is likely that evaluation will be demonstrated by a consideration of the drawbacks of the strategy and the scale of those drawbacks. Some outstanding candidates might consider that the drawbacks may be of a different size over different time periods, therefore it is difficult to judge whether it is likely to be a success.

Level	Descriptor
No mark	Non-rewardable material. No mark is to be awarded if the candidate just re-states the question, i.e. using the Internet will increase the competitiveness of the Saltash Toy Box.
Level 1 1-2 marks	Reference to one effect is given with some weak development or two effects are given with limited or no development of either. If there is just a simple judgement/value attached to one of the effects, 1 mark should be awarded. If this judgement/point has some simple support, the response should be placed at the top of this level.
Level 2 3-5 marks	Reference to two effects is given, with some development of at least one at the lower end. A judgement/point is given at the lower end of the level with some development/support, which includes at least one reason/cause/consequence, etc. At the middle of the level this analysis will be relevant and linked to the judgement/point made. Not simply making more money/profit. Answers at the middle of this level will tend to assume that the judgement/point made will work and that the change of focus will have no downside. At the top of the level there will be some evidence of balance to the point/judgement in the form of advantage/disadvantage, cost/benefit, pro/con or some counterbalancing factor. At the top of the level, candidates will attach some value/importance to one of the effects.
Level 3 6-8 marks	Reference to two effects is given with development of each. A judgement/point is given with some development which includes at least two reasons/causes/consequences, etc. and the use of the 'it depends' rule. Some balance will be given in the form of advantage/disadvantage, pros/cons, costs/benefits. The candidate will be able to show some appreciation that the effects are not 'inevitable' or 'automatic'. At this level, candidates will attach some value/importance to both of the benefits and may make a judgement about which of the effects is more important/valuable to Saltash Toy Box.

Mark schemes for 'Assess' questions (p75)
Indicative content

The aim here is for candidates to consider whether profit is the best measure of business success. The question asks the candidate to 'assess', so the candidate must develop some evidence of balance within the answer. This could take the form of alternative measures of success or through a consideration of the extent to which profit is likely to be a good measure.

Benefits of profit as a measure of success:

- Confirms business strategy is successful as revenue exceeds costs.

- Retained profit can be used for future expansion.

- Comparing profit with that of different businesses is a useful indicator of success.

However, profit is not the only measure of success. It is likely that evaluation will be demonstrated by a consideration of alternative measures of success. These include:

- Revenue.

- Market share.

- Social success – ethical and environmental indicators.

Level	Descriptor
No mark	Non-rewardable material. No mark is to be awarded if the candidate just re-states the question.
Level 1 1-2 marks	Reference to one reason is given with some weak development or two reasons are given with limited or no development of either. If there is just a simple judgement/value attached to one of the reasons, 1 mark should be awarded. If this judgement/point has some simple support, the response should be placed at the top of this level.
Level 2 3-5 marks	Reference to two reasons is given, with some development of at least one at the lower end. A judgement/point is given at the lower end of the level with some development/support, which includes at least one reason/cause/consequence, etc. At the middle of the level this analysis will be relevant and linked to the judgement/point made. Not simply making more money/profit. Answers at the middle of this level will tend to assume that the judgement/point made will work and that the change of focus will have no downside. At the top of the level there will be some evidence of balance to the point/judgement in the form of advantage/disadvantage, cost/benefit, pro/con or some counterbalancing factor. At the top of the level, candidates will attach some value/importance to one of the reasons.
Level 3 6-8 marks	Reference to two reasons is given with development of each. A judgement/point is given with some development which includes at least two reasons/causes/consequences etc. and the use of the 'it depends' rule. Some balance will be given in the form of advantage/disadvantage, pros/cons, costs/benefits. The candidate will be able to show some appreciation that the reasons are not 'inevitable' or 'automatic'. At this level, candidates will attach some value/importance to both of the benefits and may make a judgement about which of the reasons is more important/valuable for different types of business.

Mark schemes for final questions (p82)
Indicative content

The aim here is for candidates to make a judgement as to which element of the marketing mix is likely to improve Megabus' ticket sales. To demonstrate the evaluative skill, candidates could consider the importance of one element of the marketing mix and contrast it with other elements. For instance, they may consider that low prices are essential, and much more important than the quality of the service. Other candidates might highlight the fact that Internet retailing (place) is very important since the cost advantages provided by this allow the price of tickets to be reduced to such low levels. Some candidates might consider time periods and suggest that in the longer term improving the product (service) quality might become more important to Megabus' ticket sales, especially if rival transport providers lower their prices. There is no right or wrong answer to this question, but candidates should aim to make a judgement which is supported. Candidates may consider the following ideas as part of their answer:

Possible reasons why elements of the marketing mix might be important:

- Price – Megabus is seen as a no-frills bus service.

- Product – Without increasing quality, other bus operators might benefit.

- Promotion – Without promotion no one will know about Megabus' low prices.

- Place – online sales enable costs to kept down.

Possible sources of balance:

- Price – it depends on how demand reacts to changes in price and what price it chooses to charge.

- Product – improving quality might increase costs, affecting prices.

- Promotion – is it that important or are low prices the most important factor?

- Place – important, but perhaps secondary to price.

Level	Descriptor
No mark	Non-rewardable material.
Level 1 1-4 marks	One relevant point is identified with some development – there can be a maximum of 4 marks if the links to the point are relevant – one mark per link (up to 3 marks for the links and 1 mark for the relevant point). An alternative route to the marks could involve a judgement being given; at the lower end of the level no support will be provided. At the top of the level some support will be given. A list of bullet points will gain a maximum of 3 marks, assuming they are all relevant.
Level 2 5-7 marks	Candidates consider the importance of one element of Megabus' marketing mix in allowing the company to improve ticket sales and offer two or more reasons/causes/consequences, etc. in support.

At the lower end of the level no value will be attached to these reasons whilst at the top of the level there will be some recognition of the value of the points made to the business, which may be in the form of offering a counterbalancing point, identifying an advantage and disadvantage, cost/benefit, pro/con, etc.

At the middle of the level a judgement/conclusion will be made but with no support and merely re-states the question.

At the top of the level candidates may offer at least one other factor to balance out the answer. At the top of the level a judgement/conclusion will be made with some support given although not drawn from the analysis and there may be reference to the context.

Level 3
8-10 marks
Candidates consider the importance of an element of the marketing mix which will allow Megabus to increase its sales and offer two or more reasons/causes/consequences, etc. in support.

At the lower end of the level some value will be attached to these reasons whilst at the top of the level there will be clear recognition of the value of the points made to the business, identifying an advantage and disadvantage, cost/benefit, pro/con, etc. or using the 'it depends' rule. At this level candidates are likely to offer at least one other factor (another element of the marketing mix) to balance out the answer.

At the middle of the level a judgement/conclusion will be made with some support drawn from the analysis.

At the top of the level a judgement/conclusion will be clearly drawn from the analysis representing a coherent argument and will refer to the context.

Mark schemes for final questions (p87)
Indicative content

The aim here is for candidates to make a judgement as to how both customers and shareholders might benefit from the growth of Greggs. The evaluative skill will be present through candidates considering the extent to which these stakeholders will gain. Expect candidates to consider the following range of answers:

Consumers (advantages)

- Wider choice of products.
- Cheaper prices due to cost savings being passed on to the customer.

Consumers (disadvantages)

- Loss of individuality of some local products/uniformity.
- Possible increase in prices due to the lack of competition.

Shareholders (advantages)

- A rise in the share price of Greggs.
- Increased profits being made as the company grows.

Shareholders (disadvantages)

- The cost to Greggs of buying Bakers Oven.
- The risk of the company becoming the source of an investigation from the Competition Commission.

Level	Descriptor
No mark	Non-rewardable material.
Level 1 1-3 marks	Answers in this level might be little more than one sentence or a response which has limited development. There will be little or no evidence of any evaluation apart from perhaps a very simplistic judgement with no support offered or limited development. The candidate explains the benefit of the growth of Greggs on only one of the stakeholders identified in the question. A candidate that only explains one benefit cannot go beyond 3 marks. Expect to see no reference to Greggs and answers limited to a generic business. A list of bullet points will get 3 marks maximum, assuming they are all relevant points.
Level 2 4-7 marks	A reasoned response that demonstrates some analysis and evaluation and may have some balance but not as developed as that at Level 3. At the bottom end of this level the candidate will have explained the benefit to both stakeholders using terminology and inter-linkages of ideas. At the lower end of this level the answer might be unbalanced with more being written in support of one option. However, if evaluation is implied or is superficial/weak, e.g. a simple reference is made to which stakeholder is more affected, the maximum mark awardable is 5. At the top end of this level the candidate will have elaborated and developed their evaluation beyond a basic/simple statement and will consider the significance to both customers and shareholders. At the top end of this level, expect to see some balance (with clear reference to Greggs), although any evaluation may still be simplistic in nature. There may be a limited conclusion which is simply a restatement of the question or no conclusion at all. An answer focusing entirely on one style can be awarded full marks in this level provided there is evidence of analysis and evaluation given.
Level 3 8-10 marks	A clear argument is presented which is balanced and refers to the extent to which both customers and shareholders will benefit from the growth of Greggs. This is likely to include at least two factors in support, some balance to show the extent and a rounded conclusion that draws the analysis together. At the very top end a conclusion will be offered that draws on the previous information and is well supported and clearly addresses the command word. Responses will have a clear evaluative slant and will recognise that one stakeholder might benefit more than the other. Expect some candidates to refer to potential drawbacks to customers and shareholders from the growth of Greggs. At the lower end a conclusion might lack development but be an attempt to draw together the analysis offered.